CONQUER
NEEDLE
PHOBIA

Simple Ways to Reduce Your Anxiety and Fear

T0356499

MARTY MARTIN

Design & Distribution by Bublish, Inc.

ISBN: 978-1-6470433-0-8 (eBook)
ISBN: 978-1-6470433-1-5 (paperback)

DISCLAIMER

Neither the publisher nor the author is engaged in rendering medical or professional advice or services to the individual reader. This book is intended as general information only and should not be used to diagnose or treat any health condition. This book is sold with the understanding that the author and publisher are not engaged in rendering psychological or other professional services. The ideas, procedures, and suggestions contained in this book are not intended as a substitute for consulting with your physician or other competent professional. The author and publisher disclaim any liability arising directly or indirectly from the use of this book.

CONTENTS

INTRODUCTION

THIS BOOK IS meant to serve as a trusted companion and resource to help you conquer your fear or phobia of needles and injections. You may be among the 30 percent of the world's population that has a fear of needles and injections. Or you may be among the 3 percent worldwide that has a phobia of needles and injections, with one of the highest lifetime prevalence rates at 6 percent in the United States (Wardenaar et al., 2017). Or you might know someone who has this fear. If you happen to be a healthcare provider whose job is to administer injections and draw blood, then this book is designed for you as well. By reading this book yourself, as a healthcare provider, you will be better able to understand the fear and anxiety that many people experience regarding injections and how you can help.

My journey with needle and injection fears and phobias began when I was a ten-year-old child, feeling completely out of control and having to endure needle pricks before having several teeth extracted. Later, as a teenager, I was jumped and stabbed by a neighboring "crew," and I was again subjected to needle pricks prior to the surgical procedures. Perhaps due to these experiences, for many years I avoided my annual dental appointments, often rescheduling them three to four times out of fear of being jabbed with a needle by the dentist. The good news is that I can now tolerate getting vaccines, needles, and shots. Along the way, even before I became a psychologist, I learned a number of strategies to combat this fear, which I will share with you in this book.

As fate would have it, years later, as an academic researcher with a doctorate in clinical psychology and a master's degree in public health, I was part of a team that was responsible for the design and delivery of interventions for kids who resisted preventive and routine dental care because of their fear of dental needles and injections. Later, in my clinical practice, I continued to work with patients who avoided dental procedures, routine vaccinations, and other medical procedures because they would "rather die than get a needle."

A colleague of mine from Tulane School of Public Health and Tropical Medicine (where we both worked for a number of years) reached out to me to inquire about developing easily accessible resources for individuals and healthcare professionals that address this particular reason why individuals are hesitant to get vaccinated. I sat back and reflected on what was already on my very full plate but felt an "internal calling" to move forward to help the many people in need of guidance about how to overcome their fear of these sometimes lifesaving procedures. Now, I find myself in a position to help others in the face of a deadly pandemic.

NEEDLE FEARS AND PHOBIAS: A PUBLIC HEALTH CHALLENGE

The COVID-19 pandemic has led to extraordinary challenges, both for individuals and for society collectively. These are volatile, uncertain, complex, and ambiguous times. The rapid and unpredictable changes and losses that have occurred reflect a volatility that we have never encountered. On a global scale, we face the uncertainty and complexity of how to administer a vaccine to 70–85 percent of the world's population—7.8 billion people. One potential barrier is the fact that in ambiguous situations, humans are inclined to favor inaction over action (Wroe et al., 2005). For those with vaccination fears and phobias, uncertainty and even dread make their inaction all the more likely (Wroe et al., 2005).

The good news is that vaccines to combat SARS-CoV-2 (the coronavirus) are being administered, and more vaccines are nearing approval by governments. COVID-19 vaccinations are potential lifesaving tools that could help us protect ourselves and those we love. The goal of achieving herd immunity (which occurs when most of a population is immune to an infectious disease, providing indirect protection to those who are not immune to the disease) seems to be within reach. The bad news is that vaccine hesitancy and needle fears and phobias may delay the establishment of herd immunity—as well as delay the protection of individuals and those who encounter them and their contagious aerosol droplets. Fortunately, however, needle and injection fears and phobias are treatable.

The World Health Organization (WHO) ranks vaccine hesitancy as one of the top health threats globally. The fear of needles and injections is a major reason why people do not get vaccinated. A recent scientific study published in the *American Journal of Infection Control* shows that fear of needles is a real perceived barrier for people who are deciding whether to get the COVID-19 vaccination (Guidry et al., 2020). Although this is not the only perceived barrier identified by scientists, it is the focus of this book.

HOW CAN THIS BOOK HELP?

. . . .

Getting vaccinated is not a single event. It involves planning the visit, anticipating the visit, going to the visit, waiting to be seen, sitting in the room where the vaccination will take place, waiting for the vaccinator, observing the vaccination being prepared, getting the vaccination, waiting for fifteen to thirty minutes after getting the vaccination at the site, and then going home, to work, or to some other destination. And you have thoughts, feelings, and behaviors throughout all of these steps—leading up to the decision to get a shot, leading up to the actual shot, during the injection, and after the vaccine has been administered. And any of these thoughts, feelings, and behaviors may contribute to your avoidance of getting vaccinated.

Despite your fear or phobia of needles and injections, you most likely feel compelled to get vaccinated against COVID-19, or you wouldn't be reading this book. *Conquer Needle Phobia* offers you practical tools to equip you to get vaccinated and help you throughout your vaccination journey. By reading this book, you will learn quick tools that you can use in moments before the any shot, during any shot, and after any shot. These quick tools will lessen your fear before you feel as if it is spiraling out of control. Most importantly, these tools are evidence based, meaning that they have been proven by scientists to work.

The tools offered to you in this book are meant to be tailored to your individual needs. Based on what you are trying to accomplish, you pick the tool that will be most helpful. For example, if you believe that looking at a needle before it is injected will make you even more fearful, then you can select several distraction techniques presented in this book. In short, the book is designed for you to select the right tools at the right time for the right situation.

Conquering your needle and injection fear or phobia begins by putting yourself in the driver's seat, rather than simply remaining a passenger and being driven by your fear or phobia. The journey you will take begins with anticipating getting vaccinated and ends with feeling relieved that you got vaccinated. Each turn along this journey demands specific tools and resources that make up your portable toolkit to conquer your needle and injection fear or phobia.

One important note: although "a specific phobia of blood/injection/injury type" is included in the American Psychiatric Association's *Diagnostic and Statistical Manual of Mental Disorders* (2013), better known as the DSM-5, and medical professionals use the term "tryanophobia" to label this type of fear, the goal of this book is not to diagnose and not to pathologize. Nevertheless, there are limits to self-help books, and it is important for you to feel confident and competent to get the help that you deserve, which may include professional treatment from a licensed healthcare provider. If you do pursue professional help, this book can be an additional resource and source of support.

DO SELF-HELP BOOKS WORK?

You may ask, "Do self-help books work?" Fair question. There is scientific evidence that self-help books do work. In particular, research has shown that self-help books are effective in helping people with anxiety disorders, including social phobia and panic disorder (Lewis et al., 2018). Although no such research has been done specifically regarding needle and injection fears and phobias, these fall under the category of anxiety disorders. Additionally, some people with needle and injection fears experience panic attacks at some point in their vaccination journey, and therefore a self-help book can be a useful component of addressing this symptom.

If you are someone who believes that self-help books serve as a source of authoritative information, inspiration, support, and helpful tips, then this book is for you. Reading self-help books to gain insight and overcome personal challenges is called bibliotherapy (Heath et al., 2005). Bibliotherapy fits within a model of "stepped care," which begins with self-monitoring and self-management and then moves up the steps of the ladder as needed, ultimately to treatment by a specialist. Bibliotherapy is on the lower rungs of the stepped care ladder. A stepped care approach that includes bibliotherapy as a resource has been proven to be effective in scientific studies overall and for treating anxiety disorder (Ho et al., 2016).

If you are seeing a counselor or therapist but want to accelerate, reinforce, or complement your existing work, then this book is also meant for you. Beyond behavioral health practitioners, this book is also a resource for any professional who performs vaccinations and injections and even for those of you who teach these skills in a health professions education or training program.

HOW TO USE THIS BOOK

Reading this book will help you to:

- understand how fears and phobias—in particular needle and injection fears and phobias—work and develop over time;
- practice evidence-based solutions to overcome your needle and injection fear or phobia; and

- apply specific tools at just the right time during your vaccination journey, your dental appointment, or your next blood draw.

The first two chapters of this book will help you to determine whether you have a fear or a phobia of needles and injections and how to know the difference between the two. The remainder of the book is organized into three sections that address the two phases of getting vaccinated—before the vaccine and during the vaccine. The two sections are as follows:

- **Section I: Tools to Use before Your Appointment.** This section discusses strategies to help you in the process of scheduling a vaccination.
- **Section II: Tools to Use during Your Appointment.** This section identifies specific strategies that you can use from the moment you check in to get vaccinated to the moment the healthcare professional withdraws the needle from your arm and places a Band-Aid or gauze on the injection site.

Each section features scientifically valid information to increase your knowledge. Knowledge is power. Knowledge melts myths. Knowledge is key—but there is more to changing your behavior than knowledge. This book also offers you concrete, evidence-based strategies to change your thinking, adjust your feelings, and modify your behaviors. Are you ready to begin your journey to conquer your needle and injection fear or phobia in order to protect you and those around you—not only from the coronavirus but also other from other illnesses like the flu? Flip to chapter 1 to find out whether you suffer from a needle and injection fear or phobia, or are simply a bit uncomfortable about getting vaccinated.

REFERENCES

American Psychiatric Association. (2013). *Diagnostic and statistical manual of mental disorders* (5th ed.). https://doi.org/10.1176/appi. books.9780890425596

Guidry, J. P. D., Laestadius, L. I., Vraga, E. K., Miller, C. A., Perrin, P. B., Burton, C. W., Ryan, M., Fuemmeler, B. F., & Carlyle, K. E. (2020). Willingness to get the COVID-19 vaccine with and without emergency use authorization. *American Journal of Infection Control*, *49*(2), 137–142.

Heath, M. A., Sheen, D., Leavy, D., Young, E., & Money, K. (2005). Bibliotherapy: A resource to facilitate emotional healing and growth. *School Psychology International*, *26*(5), 563–580. https://doi. org/10.1177/0143034305060792

Ho, F. Y. Y., Yeung, W. F., Ng, T. H. Y., & Chan, C. S. (2016). The efficacy and cost-effectiveness of stepped care prevention and treatment for depressive and/or anxiety disorders: A systematic review and meta-analysis. *Scientific Reports*, *6*(1), 1–10.

Lewis, C., Pearce, J., & Bisson, J. I. (2018). Efficacy, cost-effectiveness, and acceptability of self-help interventions for anxiety disorders: Systematic review. *The British Journal of Psychiatry*, *200*(1), 15–21.

Wardenaar, K. J., Lim, C. C., Al-Hamzawi, A. O., Alonso, J., Andrade, L. H., Benjet, C., Bunting, B., de Girolamo, G., Demyttenaere, K., Florescu, S. E., Gureje, O., Hisateru, T., Hu, C., Huang, Y., Karam, E., Kiejna, A., Lepine, J. P., Navarro-Mateu, F., Oakley Browne, M., . . . De Jonge, P. (2017). The cross-national epidemiology of specific phobia in the World Mental Health Surveys. *Psychological Medicine, 47*(10), 1744.

l, A. L., Bhan, A., Salkovskis, P., & Bedford, H. (2005). Feeling bad about immunising our children. *Vaccine, 23*(12), 1428–1433. https://doi.org/10.1016/j.vaccine.2004.10.004

SECTION I

TOOLS TO USE BEFORE YOUR APPOINTMENT

CHAPTER 1

DO I HAVE A FEAR OR PHOBIA OF NEEDLES AND INJECTIONS?

DISCOMFORT ABOUT GETTING a shot is natural and normal. It's reasonable to see how anyone may be hesitant about another person sticking a needle in their arm. As humans, we are designed to protect ourselves against threats—real or imagined. Seeing another person armed with a syringe and a needle is likely to trigger a protective reaction, even if only for a few seconds. Yet, for many, this protective reaction is much stronger and can be characterized as a fear or phobia. In this chapter, you'll find tools to help determine if that's the case for you. First, however, we will explore answers to some common questions.

QUESTIONS AND ANSWERS ABOUT
THE VACCINATION EXPERIENCE

Before you explore whether you do indeed have a fear or phobia of needles and injections, it's helpful to consider some typical reactions to the vaccination experience. Let's explore some common questions about vaccinations.

Are there specific parts of the vaccination experience that are more troublesome than others?

You might be surprised to know that it's not always the injection itself that's the most anxiety-producing part of the experience. For some, it is the scheduling; for others, it's waiting to be called into the room; and for others, it's the needle being withdrawn from their arm.

Is it normal to feel pain?

Yes.

When being stuck with a needle and then injected with medication, some people will experience just a poke—the physical sensation of the prick of the needle. Others are likely to experience a more intense physical sensation. This intensity is often perceived as pain. As humans, we are designed to avoid physical pain. This is normal and natural.

Is it normal to feel the medicine being injected?

Yes, for some. No, for others.

After being stuck with the needle, most people experience a bit of discomfort while the medication is injected. We may express this discomfort by looking away, closing our eyes, or tensing up. This is normal and natural. Others may look directly at the needle, closely observing how fast or slow the medication is being injected from the syringe into their arm. Although the time span is several seconds, the perceived time is much longer.

What will I experience after the injection?

After all the medication has been injected into the arm, some people don't give it another thought and are ready to move on with their day, but most people experience a combination of any of these feelings:

- a sense of relief
- a sense of mastery
- a sense of enhanced protection

Some people may be on the alert for any blood, even the smallest amount. Others may look for a hole in their skin. A few, especially those who have hair or thin skin at the site of the injection, may be concerned about the technician wiping their skin with alcohol and placing the Band-Aid, or they may worry about having to remove the Band-Aid or the gauze and tape later. And an exceedingly small number of people may be worried about whether any blood will appear on their shirt or blouse and then "ruin their clothes." Finally, for vaccines, you may feel some soreness at the site of the injection for one to two days.

Anxiety is triggered by how we frame an experience, such as getting vaccinated. If you choose to frame the situation as "terrifying," then your body will turn on the fight, flight, or freeze response to protect you from the threat. On the other hand, if you choose to frame the situation as "uncomfortable but tolerable," then your body will be on alert, but your fight, flight, or freeze response will not be activated. If this response is not activated, then you will not experience distress.

DO I REALLY HAVE A NEEDLE PHOBIA?

You may have always been told that you have a needle phobia, but don't assume that this is true. Take the two self-assessments below to understand whether your response to needles and injections constitutes a worry, a bit of anxiety, a fear, or a phobia. Keep in mind, though, that these assessments should not take the place of an evaluation by a mental health professional. Rather, the purpose here is to help you determine whether you may have a fear or phobia.

SELF-ASSESSMENT 1:
NERVOUSNESS, FEAR, OR PHOBIA

Look at the pictures below and then rate how you feel by answering either A, B, or C.

Key:

    A. It didn't bother me at all.
    B. I found it somewhat disturbing.
    C. I could hardly look at it without feeling anxious or repulsed.

Picture 1 Rating: _____

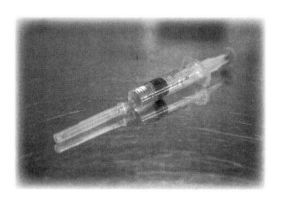

Picture 2 Rating: _____

Picture 3 Rating: _____

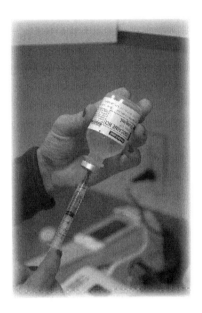

Picture 4 Rating: _____

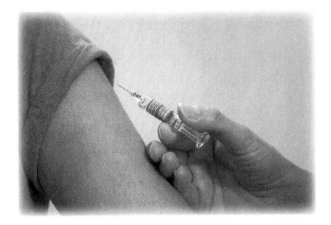

Picture 5 Rating: _____

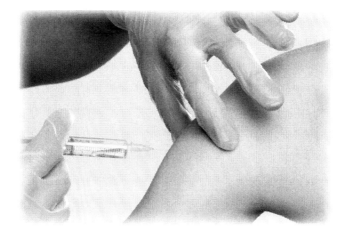

Picture 6 Rating: _____

Picture 7 Rating: _____

ANSWER SHEET

Picture Number	Place an X If You Answered B	Place an X If You Answered C
1		
2		
3		
4		
5		
6		
7		
	Number of X's:	Number of X's:

SCORING

If you have more than three *x*'s for B and more than two *x*'s for C, then you are likely to experience some level of needle and injection fear or phobia. Now, take the next self-assessment tool.

SELF-ASSESSMENT 2: INJECTION PHOBIA SCALE–SHORT FORM

This tool was developed by a group of researchers at Vanderbilt University. It is derived from the eighteen-item Injection Phobia Scale–Anxiety Scale, which is psychometrically validated, meaning that scientific studies have demonstrated that it is a valid way to measure (Olatunji et al., 2010). This is not a diagnostic tool.

DIRECTIONS

Below is a description of a number of situations in which persons with injection phobia can experience anxiety or fear. Read each item and rate on a scale from 0 to 4 how much anxiety you would experience if you were in the situation.

	No Anxiety			Max Anxiety	
1. Giving a blood sample by having a finger pricked	0	1	2	3	4
2. Having a shot in the upper arm	0	1	2	3	4
3. Having an anesthetic injection at the dentist	0	1	2	3	4
4. Having a venipuncture (needle inserted into vein)	0	1	2	3	4
5. Getting an injection in the buttock	0	1	2	3	4
6. Getting ears pierced	0	1	2	3	4
7. Getting a vaccination	0	1	2	3	4
8. Getting an intravenous injection	0	1	2	3	4

Copyright Permission: olubunmi.o.olatunji@vanderbilt.edu

Permission granted by Dr. Olatunji to use this tool.

WHAT DOES MY SCORE MEAN?

0–7	8–22	23–30
You are not that anxious about needles and injections. It is normal to feel a bit nervous.	You are moderately anxious about needles and injections. Your feelings are a bit more than the normal feelings of nervousness.	You are indeed anxious about needles and injections to the point that you might avoid injections including vaccines.

Let's look specifically at item 7 on the assessment: getting a vaccination. If you rated this question a 0,1, or 2, this means that anxiety and fear will not stop you from getting vaccinated. If you rated this question a 3 or 4, this means your anxiety, fear, and perhaps phobic response to getting vaccinated may stop you from protecting yourself and others by getting vaccinated.

When you rate the items on the Injection Phobia Scale–Short Form, you may be surprised by what seem like contradictory responses. For example, I rated getting an anesthetic injection at the dentist a 4 but rated all the other seven items a 0 or 1. Knowing this about myself, I have used most of the recommendations in this book to help me handle going to the dentist even though I know at times I will need to get an anesthetic shot.

SHOULD I GET HELP FROM A HEALTHCARE PROFESSIONAL?

If, after taking both self-assessment tools, you feel that you need to supplement this book with professional help, then do so. You may need more support than this book can offer you, and there are many types of healthcare professionals who can assist you. I would recommend that you check out the following therapist directories:

- Anxiety and Depression Association of America: Find a Therapist Directory
- Association for Behavioral and Cognitive Therapies: Find a CBT Therapist
- Psychology Today: Find a Cognitive Behavioral (CBT) Therapist
- Society of Clinical Psychology: Therapist Directory

When looking for a therapist, look for those who mention any of these specializations or techniques in their profile:

- specific phobia
- needle and injection phobia
- medical phobia
- exposure therapy
- participant modeling
- guided mastery
- applied muscle tension
- virtual reality exposure (VRT)
- systematic desensitization

HIGHLIGHTS TO RECALL

You now should have a better understanding of how nervousness, anxiety, fears, and phobias work overall and in response to getting a shot. Here are two key points from this chapter to keep in mind:

- It is normal and natural to feel a bit of nervousness about getting a vaccine or other injection.
- Understanding typical responses to the various steps involved in getting a vaccination is helpful in learning how to minimize your own anxiety, fear, or phobia.

It's not about courage. It's about knowing how anxiety, fears, and phobias work and then using the tools in this book to face the situation. In chapter 2, you'll learn more about how anxiety, fears, and phobias of needles and injections work and how to tell the difference between fears and phobias.

REFERENCES

Olatunji, B. O., Sawchuk, C. N., Moretz, M. W., David, B., Armstrong, T., & Ciesielski, B. G. (2010). Factor structure and psychometric properties of the Injection Phobia Scale–Anxiety. *Psychological Assessment, 22*(1), 167.

CHAPTER 2

NEEDLE AND INJECTION FEARS AND PHOBIAS 101

IMAGINE THAT YOU hear about a person who has rescheduled their vaccination appointment three times. Is this person just nervous, a bit fearful, somewhat anxious, or phobic? Admittedly, language can be confusing. In this case, we might assume that the person is phobic. Why? They have avoided this specific "feared" situation three times. By avoiding getting the vaccine, this person is hindering their ability to get something important in their lives. This chapter is intended to educate you about needle and injection fears and phobias. By the end of this chapter, you will be aware of the difference. While both can make you feel uncomfortable, they are vastly different.

VACCINATION EXPERIENCE: YOUR EXPERIENCE

Envision that you are seated in a stiff chair in your doctor's or nurse practitioner's office. Your body stiffens a bit, in part due to the coldness of the exam room. A vaccinator enters into the room, seemingly at the same time you hear the knock on the door, and without looking in your eyes, asks, "Are you ready for your vaccine?" You suddenly notice the silver tray with a needle and a bottle of what is probably the vaccine. You respond, "I guess so . . . as ready as I'll ever be" as your smile widens a bit, trying to catch a glimpse of the nurse's eyes to make human-to-human contact. The nurse requests that you roll your sleeve up. You do so, wondering if you have rolled it up far enough. A faint whiff of alcohol hits you along with the cold swish and quick pressure of the nurse cleaning the area on your arm around where the needle will be inserted into your skin. You now feel a little pressure as the nurse pulls together the skin around the cleansed surface with one hand, while holding the needle in the other hand. You know that the needle is about to meet and enter your skin and that the vaccine will be injected through the needle. As if on autopilot, you turn your head away from observing what you already know is about to happen, and then you feel it—the pinch. It is as if your entire world is centered on the injection and you feel a bit of pressure. It is as if this less-than-five-second experience is being projected frame by frame, second by second, moment by moment. Suddenly, as the needle is removed, you experience a sense of profound relief and notice that you were holding your breath for what seemed like an eternity.

SELF-REFLECTION: HOW DID YOU FEEL ABOUT WHAT YOU JUST READ?

Reflect for a moment about what you just read. Then choose which of the following most closely matches your experience while simply reading this passage:

- nothing out of the ordinary
- nervous
- fearful
- anxious
- phobic

There is no right or wrong way to feel after reading this passage about the experience of receiving a vaccination. Yet, if you were to ask one hundred people to read this passage, just as you have read this passage, you know that everybody would not have the same internal experience. The reason people have different responses to the same situation is because of the way they perceive that situation. You shape *the experience*, but the experience does not have to *shape you*. Psychologists refer to this as "cognitive appraisal."

COGNITIVE APPRAISAL: MAKING SENSE OF WHAT HAPPENS TO US

Two psychologists, Dr. Richard Lazarus and Dr. Susan Folkman, wrote in their book *Stress, Appraisal, and Coping* that our internal response to situations depends upon how we view (or appraise) the situation. The diagram below walks you through how cognitive appraisal works in situations where you choose to get a shot, injection, or vaccine.

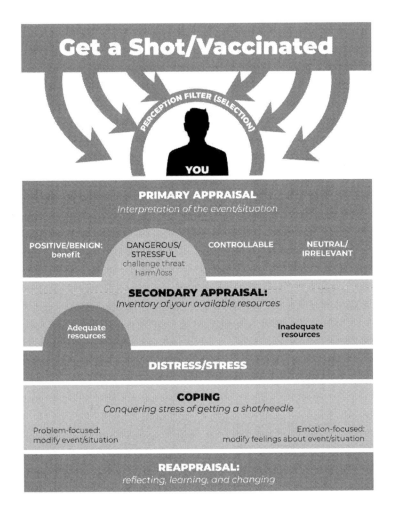

Cognitive appraisal is the process in which you evaluate how a particular situation, such as getting a vaccine, most closely fits into the three primary categories below:

- positive or benign
- dangerous
- irrelevant

As you look at the diagram above, how do you view getting a vaccine or shot—as positive or benign, dangerous, or irrelevant? Or does it depend on certain internal and external factors? Now, let us turn our attention to primary appraisal.

Primary Appraisal

Positive or benign appraisals occur when you regard the situation as potentially beneficial to your health and well-being. Dangerous appraisals occur when you view the situation as stressful, harmful, or as a loss. The loss could be a loss of control; for example, if your employer requires that you show proof of vaccination before returning to work. Finally, irrelevant appraisals occur when you view the situation as neither positive or benign nor dangerous or stressful.

For those of you who have a needle and injection fear or phobia, you are likely to agree that you characterize this situation as threatening or dangerous, recognizing that "danger" is not all or none but that there are degrees of danger. When confronted with a perceived or real threat, it is natural and normal to go into a state of hypervigilance. You are on the lookout, you are ready for what may come next, and your protective radar is turned on. Researchers now reveal that hypervigilance occurs in those who have needle and injection phobias (Buodo, Peyk, Junghöfer, Palomba, & Rockstroh, 2007). In this book, you will learn to challenge your primary appraisal by reflecting upon the following questions when you are in a situation with a needle, injection, or vaccine:

- Is there a short- or long-term benefit?
- Is there a short- or long-term harm or cost?
- Is this not a big deal?
- Am I making a "mountain out of a molehill"?

If you are asking and thinking about these questions and still feel a sense of threat and danger, then this is when the secondary appraisal becomes key to coping effectively.

Secondary Appraisal

In the secondary appraisal, you evaluate what you can do to overcome or prevent harm or loss. You also use the coping resources available to you to improve your chance of success or your enjoyment the benefits. Benefits may be short-term (such as the feeling of mastery after getting vaccinated) or long-term (such as decreasing the likelihood of getting the virus and spreading it to those you care about).

COPING: RESOURCES MAKE THE DIFFERENCE

Coping, in this situation, is defined as the capacity to meet the demands of getting vaccinated by fully utilizing all the resources available to you personally and from others in your circle (Lazarus & Folkman, 1984b). Coping does not mean that you will not experience the demands of the situation. Rather, it means that your resources are greater than the demands and that you can address the challenge head-on.

Therefore, a word of caution is warranted. Not all coping is healthy or productive. As an example, let us imagine that for you to "get through" a shot, you get drunk or high before getting the shot. This coping tool may help you "get through," but the cost of relying on this dysfunctional coping tool may reveal itself in the short or long run. More effective and healthier coping tools are presented in this book to help you to not only rise to the challenge of getting the shot but also strengthen your ability to cope using healthy coping resources.

TWO SHADES OF COPING:
PROBLEM AND EMOTION FOCUSED

Coping has two widely recognized major functions: altering the troubled person-environment relation that is causing the distress (problem-focused coping) and regulating stressful emotions (emotion-focused coping). Two previous studies provide strong empirical support for the idea that coping usually includes both functions. Both forms of coping were represented in over 98 percent of the stressful encounters reported by middle-aged men and women (Folkman & Lazarus, 1980) and in an average of 96 percent of the self-reports of how college students coped with a stressful examination (Folkman & Lazarus, 1985).

You have a toolkit of coping resources to help you meet any demand you encounter. Some of the coping resources seek to figure out what to do to meet the challenge—that is problem-focused coping. Other coping resources aim to decrease stress and increase the tolerability of the challenge—that is emotion-focused coping. Psychologists tell us that it is best to use problem-focused coping when there is a greater degree of control in the situation or when there are specific coping resources you can use. For instance, while you are receiving a vaccine, you have control over how to choose to cope with the situation. For example, you can choose to distract yourself or close your eyes. However, it is best to use emotion-focused coping when you find yourself in a situation in which your control is limited or nonexistent or you lack the coping resources at that time. For instance, you accidentally cut yourself with an old knife and need to visit the ER, where they suddenly give you a tetanus shot while simultaneously attending to your open wound.

WORDS MATTER: FEAR, ANXIETY, AND PHOBIA

It may be helpful to review scientific definitions of fear, anxiety, and phobia, as these terms are related but are not the same.

Fear

Fear is natural and normal. It is expected when exposed to known threats such as a snake or needle. However, anxiety is also the anticipation of a future threat such as waiting to be called to get blood drawn.

Fear is an emotional reaction triggered by a known sign of danger. Once activated, your body responds by releasing biochemicals and your goal is to escape in order to avoid the danger.

Anxiety

Fear is short lived. Anxiety lasts longer. Like fear, anxiety is normal and natural. Yet, there's a catch. If the anxiety prevents you from engaging in school, work, family, and other obligations, then this type of anxiety requires an intervention. Anxiety reaches an unhealthy level when it prevents you from living your life in some way.

Fear/Anxiety Connection

Fear is a core feature of anxiety. Fear is not all or none. Fear is experienced along a continuum, from not at all consuming to all-consuming. When the level of fear alters your way of life, this is a sign of anxiety. For example, you reschedule your dental appointment three times because you are scared to death of needles. When fear is inappropriate for the situation, this is a sign of anxiety. Another outcome of fear and anxiety is how you respond. For example, if the only coping resource that worked in the past when getting a shot was to scream and run away down the hall, then this may have worked when you were younger but probably not as an adult. The key is to increase the number and variety of constructive coping responses to overcome or lessen your fear and anxiety.

Unlike fear, which has a specific focus and rapidly disappears when the threat is gone, anxiety is often not tied to a specific focus and generally lasts longer (Kalat & Shiota, 2007). Remember, fear and anxiety are interconnected.

Phobia

Fear focuses on a specific sign of danger or threat, whereas a phobia's focus is like a laser on a very particular sign of danger or threat, typically an object such as a needle. Phobias are more intense than fears. That is, the fear is so great that it is disproportionate to the situation. For instance, many people are not thrilled about getting a vaccine, but they manage to get it done. Those with needle and injection phobia typically do not. Those with phobias will experience intense fear and engage in avoidance behaviors regardless of whether they are in a situation saturated with the real or perceived danger or they anticipate that they will be in that situation. Those with needle and injection phobia start worrying about the upcoming appointment a couple of weeks or days before they are scheduled to receive the vaccine. In short, people with phobias try to avoid what they are afraid of.

Signs of Phobia

You may wonder if you have a phobia. Reflect on chapter 1, when you took the self-assessments. Below is a list of several common signs of phobia, including needle and injection phobia. As you read the list, check off in your mind whether you experience that feeling by even thinking about getting a shot or vaccine.

Common signs of phobia:

- panic and fear
- rapid heartbeat
- shortness of breath
- dizziness or light-headedness
- trembling
- a strong desire to get away

The good news is that there are healthy, adaptive coping resources that you can use to lessen these symptoms and to reduce the negative impact of needle and injection phobia. The next section of this book first provides you with a guide to help you understand how phobias develop and, more importantly, new tools to add to your toolkit.

CORONAPHOBIA: CORONAVIRUS ANXIETY

The novel coronavirus (SARS-CoV-2) emerged as a new virus, which resulted in a new infectious disease that we now call COVID-19. Researchers have discovered a new phobia—coronaphobia, which is anxiety related to coronavirus (Asmundson & Taylor, 2020).

PHOBIAS: CAUSES AND ROOTS

There does not seem to be one cause of phobias, but there are several factors that might play a part in their development. Research tell us that blood-injection-injury phobia develops via multiple pathways

(Jessup, Tomarken, Viar-Paxton, & Olatunji, 2020). Below are eight possible paths that lead to the development of an intense fear or phobia of needles, shots, injections, and vaccines.

Genetics and Family

- Genetics – Some people appear to be born with a tendency to be more anxious than others, which can develop into a phobia.
- Family environment – Parents who are very worried or anxious can influence the way you cope with anxiety later in life, and you may even develop the same phobia as a parent or older sibling.

Trauma

- A specific incident – For instance, if you encountered a lot of turbulence on a plane at a young age without adequate comfort, you might later develop a phobia about flying.
- Trauma – If you experienced abuse in a particular setting, you may develop a phobia about similar places or an object that you associate with the abuse.

Observational/Learning

- Vicarious – You can also develop a phobia from observing others who are going through a traumatic event.
- Hearing about a traumatic event – If there is a lot of talk or media coverage about a threatening or traumatic event, such as a plane crash, you can develop a phobia relating to that topic.

Stress Response

- Responses to panic or fear – If you have a strong reaction, like a panic attack, in response to a particular situation or object, and you find this embarrassing or people around you react strongly, this can cause you to develop a more intense anxiety about being in that situation again.
- Long-term/chronic stress – This can cause feelings of anxiety and depression and reduce your ability to cope with all types of situations. Why? When you have chronic stress, it can feel as if you never quite settle down. You may feel drained. You may feel spent. This can make you feel more fearful or anxious about being in a challenging situation, such as getting a vaccination, because your "battery is drained."

You may not know or recall the specific reason your phobia developed. You do not have to know the reason for your needle and injection fear or phobia to do something about it. You do not need to figure it out before trying to decrease the distress associated with your needle and injection fear or phobia. Try not to blame yourself, shame yourself, or beat yourself up.

IT'S OKAY TO BE FEARFUL AND EVEN PHOBIC ABOUT NEEDLES, SHOTS, INJECTIONS, AND VACCINES

The key is that if you are fearful about getting vaccinated, then that's okay. If you are anxious about getting vaccinated, then that's okay. If you are terrified about getting vaccinated, then that's probably not okay, but it can be okay, which you will learn by reading this book. If you fail to schedule a vaccination, fail to keep your scheduled appointment, or feign some type of illness or emergency right before you get vaccinated, then that's not okay, but it can be okay, which you will learn by reading this book.

What does "okay" mean?

"Okay" means that if you allow yourself to feel what you feel but you get vaccinated even though you feel that discomfort, stress, fear, or some anxiety, then that's normal and expected. The key is to view getting the vaccination as a challenge, remembering that you are in control and that there are concrete benefits for you and others after you get vaccinated.

TYPES OF NEEDLE FEARS OR PHOBIAS

If you have a needle and injection phobia, then recognize that not everybody experiences it in the same way. First, you are a unique individual; therefore, the way your phobia presents itself will be unique. Second, there are four types of needle and injection phobia (Khan, Memon, Rehman, Muhammad, & Ali, 2015). Learn about these four types while asking yourself this question: "Which type describes me the most?"

- Vasovagal – Afflicts up to 50 percent of those with a phobia and, hence, is the most common. It is a genetically acquired reflex reaction. This type of phobia is uniquely characterized by light-headedness, dizziness, and even fainting. For some who experience these symptoms, there may be a "fear of fear" about fainting. This "fear of fear" must be watched carefully so that it does not convert into panic attacks (Clark, 1986).

- Associative – Afflicts up to 30 percent of those with a phobia and, hence, is the second most common (Mohammed, Hassane, & Mohamed, 2017). It arises from directly experiencing or witnessing another person undergo a traumatic dental or medical procedure and in individuals who associate such a painful procedure involving needles with past negative experiences. This type of phobia is learned. Because it's learned, it can then be unlearned.

- Resistive – Afflicts up to 20 percent of those with a phobia, and, hence, is the third most common. It's characterized by the fear of needles and being controlled or restrained (Mohammed et al., 2017). The feeling of being controlled or restrained can be physical, emotional, or psychological. It arises from poor handling and experiences of being forced emotionally or physically. This type of phobia is strongly associated with a traumatic event, often during childhood or adolescence.

- Hyperalgesic – Afflicts up to 10 percent of those with a phobia, and it can be inherited. It arises from hypersensitivity not to a needle, but to a sensation of pain (Ziegler, Magerl, Meyer, & Treede, 1999). This is the fear of pain associated with a medical or dental procedure (Aslaksen & Lyby, 2015).

Table 1 shows you the best way to approach needle phobia, depending on the type, in order to make it easier for you to get a shot, an injection, or vaccinated.

Table 1

Phobia Type	Recommended Treatment/Tools
Vasovagal	• Applied Tension Technique (Ditto, Byrne, & Holly, 2009)
Associative	• Cognitive Therapy • Hypnosis • Antianxiety medication (Ayala et al., 2009)
Resistive	• Psychotherapy • Self-Injection • Trusted healthcare provider (Hogan, Kikuta, & Taddio, 2010)
Hyperalgesic	• Anesthesia, topical or general (Ditto et al., 2009; Hogan et al., 2010)

All these treatments and tools will be covered in this book, except for medication and anesthesia. Psychotherapy will also not be covered, but several psychotherapeutic methods will be covered.

HIGHLIGHTS TO RECALL

You should now have a better understanding of how fears and phobias are related and yet different. Two key points from this chapter are as follows:

- Fears and phobias exist along a continuum, with fear at one end and phobia at the other end.
- With a phobia, fear is greater in severity than the actual threat posed.

Now that you know how anxiety, fears, and phobias work in the case of needles and injections, it is time to turn your attention to creating your toolkit to conquer these fears and phobias. In chapter 3, you will learn about the specific tools you can use to prepare yourself to make your initial appointment and show up to get a vaccine or another shot.

REFERENCES

Aslaksen, P.M. & Lyby, P.S. (2015). Fear of pain potentiates nocebo hyperalgesia. *Journal of Pain Research*, 8, 703–710.

Asmundson, G.J.G. & Taylor, S. (2020). Coronaphobia: Fear and the 2019-nCoV outbreak. *Journal of Anxiety Disorders*, 70. http:, 102196. Crossref.

Ayala, E.S., Meuret, A.E., Ritz, T. (2009). Treatments for blood-injury-injection phobia: A critical review of current evidence. *Journal of Psychiatric Research*, 43 (15), 1235–1242.

Buodo, G., Peyk, P., Junghöfer, M., Palomba, D., & Rockstroh, B. (2007). Electromagnetic indication of hypervigilant responses to emotional stimuli in blood-injection-injury fear. *Neuroscience Letters*, 424 (2), 100–105.

Clark, D.M. (1986). A cognitive approach to panic. *Behaviour Research and Therapy*, 24 (4), 461–470.

Ditto, B., Byrne, N., Holly, C. (2009). "Physiological correlates of applied tension may contribute to reduced fainting during medical procedures." *Annals of Behavioral Medicine,* 37 (3), 306–314. Crossref. PMID 19730965.

Hogan, M.E.; et al. (10 February 2010). "A systematic review of measures for reducing injection pain during adult immunization." *Vaccine.* (2009), 28 (6), 1514–1521. Crossref. PMID 20003927.

Jessup, S.C., Tomarken, A., Viar-Paxton, M.A., & Olatunji, B.O. (2020). Effects of repeated exposure to fearful and disgusting stimuli on fear renewal in blood-injection-injury phobia. *Journal of Anxiety Disorders,* 74, 102272. Crossref.

Kahn, F., Memon, B.A., Rehman, H., Muhammad, S.S., & Ali, A. (2015). Prevalence of needle phobia among young patients presenting to tertiary care government hospitals of Karachi, Pakistan. *International Journal of Research,* 2 (1), 127–135.

Kalat, J.W. & Shiota, M.N. Emotion. Belmont, CA: Thomson Wadsworth, 2007.

Lazarus, R.S. & Folkman, S. Stress, appraisal, and coping. New York: Spring Publishing Company, 1984.

Mohammed, H.M., Hassane, A., & Mohamed, A.H. (2017). Nursing innovations: Painless IM injection. *International Journal of Novel Research in Healthcare and Nursing,* 4 (1), 129–137.

Ziegler, E.A., Magerl, W., Meyer, R.A., & Treede, R.D. (1999). Secondary hyperalgesia to punctate mechanical stimuli: central sensitization to A-fibre nociceptor input. *Brain,* 122 (12), 2245–2257.

CHAPTER 3

THE APPLIED TENSION TECHNIQUE

"A GOLD STANDARD" is a phrase that is used by healthcare professionals to describe a tool or technique that has been scientifically proven to work. The applied tension technique (ATT) is regarded as a gold standard treatment for those experiencing needle and injection fears and even phobias. This does not mean that this technique works all the time for everybody in all situations. It does mean that this tool or technique is worth investing your time in, learning how to perform and even master it to reap the benefits. This investment is highly likely to reward you now and in the future.

After reading chapter 3, you will be able to answer the following questions easily:

- What is the ATT?
- How does the ATT work?

- Why is the ATT able to effectively dissolve an individual's fear of needles and injections?

Additionally, you will learn how to use this technique when necessary.

Not only will the answers to the aforementioned questions guide you in using ATT, you will also be introduced to the deliberate practice mindset, which will serve as the foundation for all the tools and techniques presented in this book. Are you ready to get started creating your toolkit? Kindly continue reading chapter 3 to see all that this chapter has to offer.

NEEDLE AND INJECTION PHOBIAS: DIFFERENT FROM OTHER PHOBIAS

Needle and injection phobias differ from other phobias partly because standard relaxation training techniques are not as effective when treating the former, compared to the latter. The risk of fainting (i.e., vasovagal syncope) is higher when individuals are exposed to blood than to needles and syringes (Sánchez-Navarro, Martínez-Selva, Maldonado, Carrillo-Verdejo, Pineda, & Torrente, 2018). Since it is different from the other phobias, you will learn a technique, called ATT, tailored to counter needle and injection phobias.

What is vasovagal syncope?

This is what is commonly referred to as "fainting." Part of the nervous system sets off a reflex in which heart rate decreases or may even stop for a few seconds (bradycardia), causing blood pressure to drop sharply (hypotension). Though this reflex is normal, some individuals are more likely to experience it. When this occurs, insufficient blood is pumped to the brain, leading to dizziness and fainting.

What are the symptoms?

The individual may turn pale, feel dizzy, become sweaty or nauseous, develop blurred vision, and may have difficulty hearing.

What can trigger fainting?

Fainting can be triggered by different stimuli:

- seeing blood or needles
- standing still
- experiencing stressful or emotional situations
- being in very warm environments
- being dehydrated or not having eaten

These are the factors that increase the chances of fainting.

Adapted from Torbay and South Devon NHS Trust: Patient Information-Torbay Hospital Service Vasovagal Syncope. Vasovagal Syncope (torbayandsouthdevon.nhs.uk)

Relaxing could make it worse

When someone has a fear of needles or blood, they are often told to relax. Further, they may even learn various relaxation techniques taught by well-meaning therapists or healthcare providers. However, individuals with a fear of needles are less responsive to relaxation techniques. Furthermore, relaxation can often have the opposite effect, as it reduces blood pressure, increasing the possibility of fainting. So, what should you do instead of using relaxation techniques? This is where the ATT comes in, as it not only decreases needle-related distress but may also prevent and rapidly respond to fainting.

The comparison between the factors related to needle and injection phobias and other phobias are shown in table 2.

Table 2: Symptom Comparison between Needle
and Injection Phobias and Other Phobias

Factors	Other Phobias	Needle/Injection Phobias
Blood pressure	Increases	Increases, then decreases
Heart rate	Fast	Increases, then decreases
Vertigo (Dizziness)	Typically not present	Common
Syncope (Fainting)	Typically not present	Common

Marks (1988). Blood-injury phobia: A review. *American Journal of Psychiatry*, 145, 1207-1213

As shown in the table above, individuals who suffer from needle and injection phobia exhibit what scientists call a "diphasic physiological response." First, there is an increase in blood pressure and heart rate, followed by a decrease. It is estimated that eight out of ten individuals who suffer from needle and injection phobia experience this unique physiological response. You can see a comparison in physiological responses between needle and injection phobias and other phobias in the table above.

You may have experienced these unpleasant symptoms in the past, and they might have been so distressing that you now avoid injections altogether, regardless of the benefits.

THE APPLIED TENSION TECHNIQUE: GOLD STANDARD

The ATT is the gold standard (or most effective treatment) to counter the diphasic physiological response. Shown below are two different strategies to apply this technique.

STRATEGY #1: APPLIED MUSCLE TENSION TECHNIQUE – INSTRUCTIONS

The ATT is easy to use by following these instructions:

1. Sit in a chair with your feet flat against the floor and your arms on the armrest.
2. Tense all major muscle groups (thighs, buttocks, stomach, arms, fists, neck, and jaw) at the same time for fifteen to twenty seconds and then release the tension. Do not try to relax your muscles beyond the level that they were before you consciously tensed them.
3. Wait five seconds and then repeat step 2.
4. Do this cycle of tension and release five times.
5. Your face may start to feel warm and turn red, since you blood pressure begins to elevate; this is an indicator that the exercise is working.
6. Practice this technique at least once daily. This will help you learn how to control your blood pressure better when needed.

As you can tell from this six-step technique, practicing before you receive an injection or venipuncture is the key to gaining greater control of your body.

STRATEGY #2: APPLIED MUSCLE TENSION TECHNIQUE – RIGHT BEFORE OR DURING THE INJECTION

According to Öst et al. (1991), patients should learn to recognize the earliest signs of a decrease in blood pressure and begin applying the ATT at that time. When experiencing the symptoms of pre-syncope which is the feeling that you may faint, you should do the following:

- Cross your legs while tensing your leg, buttock, and abdominal muscles for five to ten seconds.
- Extend your legs isometrically (e.g., hold them stable) while receiving an injection or during a venipuncture.
- Hold a rubber ball in the hand you use to write. Squeeze the ball as long as you can or until your symptoms disappear.
- Tense your arms by gripping one hand with the other and pull them away from each other without letting go. Hold the grip as long as you can or until your symptoms disappear.

If you experience any dizziness or feel like you are about to faint at any point, take **immediate action**:

- Sit down **immediately**.
- If possible, **lie down flat**.
- **Squat** if you are unable to lie down.
- Preferably, **elevate your legs**.

- **Tense and release** your calf muscles (this helps increase your blood pressure).
- Once your symptoms subside, **carefully** stand up. If you experience further symptoms, sit or lie down again.
- **If your symptoms are mild**, try wriggling your toes, clenching your fists, and tensing your calf muscles until said symptoms subside.

Adapted: Torbay and South Devon NHS Trust: Patient Information-Torbay Hospital Service Vasovagal Syncope. Vasovagal Syncope (torbayandsouthdevon.nhs.uk)

Both strategies can increase your perceptions of self-control. As we will see in chapter 5, when you increase your perceived control, the likelihood of fainting is reduced (Gilchrist, McGovern, Bekkouche, Bacon, & Ditto, 2015).

HIGHLIGHTS TO RECALL

Many concepts are presented in this chapter on ATT. Below are a few key highlights for you to remember to enhance your ability to use ATT as a tool before a vaccine and injection, or even during a vaccine and injection.

- ATT may prevent you from feeling dizzy and fainting by delaying your vasovagal response and increasing your blood pressure.
- ATT simply involves alternating between tensing and releasing major muscle groups in the body (e.g., arms, legs, and stomach).

- ATT is an effective method against needle and injection phobia.

You have now added an important tool, the ATT, to your toolkit. When you read chapter 5 on exposure therapy, you will learn why ATT is essential to receiving the most benefits from exposure therapy, which is the focus of that chapter. In fact, using the two combined techniques offers additional benefits. We shall now turn our attention to a topic that may spark your curiosity and interest—hypnosis. In the next chapter, you will learn not only the power of hypnosis but also how to hypnotize yourself. Yes. Hypnotize yourself.

TIPS FOR EDUCATORS, HEALTHCARE PROFESSIONALS, AND THERAPISTS

The ATT is one of two evidence-based treatments for needle and injection phobia (Jiang, Upton, & Newby, 2020), the other being exposure therapy, which is detailed in chapter 5.

- The ATT has demonstrated efficacy in the treatment of needle phobias (Ayala, Meuret, & Ritz, 2009; McMurtry et al., 2016).
- Employ the ATT if you are aware that the patient has a history of vasovagal syncope or any of these symptoms: light-headedness, dizziness, or fainting (McMurtry et al., 2016).
- Using the ATT in combination with exposure therapy has proven greatly effective (McMurtry et al., 2016).

The clinical rationale for employing the ATT has been described in a clinical practice guideline for the treatment of needle fear as described below:

> Muscle tension is a technique designed to raise blood pressure for individuals with a history of fainting; as noted previously, vasovagal syncope is more common in individuals with blood-injection-injury phobia than the typical population or populations with other phobias. The addition of muscle tension to exposure-based therapy is referred to as applied tension (McMurtry et al., 2016, p. 230).

This evidence-based, clinical technique is unique in the treatment of vasovagal syncope, which occurs due to blood-injury-injection phobia.

Below is a table that you may find useful to reduce the likelihood that the individual will faint while being injected. These evidence-based techniques are complementary to ATT and increase perceived control.

Table 3

Patient education (Marchiondo, 2010)	Offer information to the individual regarding vasovagal syncope and provide them with techniques to decrease the likelihood of fainting before and during injection or venipuncture.

Water consumption (France et al., 2010)	Encourage the individual to drink about sixteen ounces of water before receiving the injection or venipuncture.
Reclining during pr after injection or venipuncture	Suggest that the individual reclines or sits down during the procedure and for fifteen to thirty minutes afterward.

REFERENCES

Ayala, E.S., Meuret, A.E., & Ritz, T. (2009). Treatments for blood-injury-injection phobia: a critical review of current evidence. *Journal of Psychiatric Research*, 43(15), 1235–1242. https://doi. https://doi.org/10.1016/j.jpsychires.2009.04.008.

France, C.R., Ditto, B., Wissel, M.E., et al. (2010). Predonation hydration and applied muscle tension combine to reduce presyncopal reactions to blood donation. *Transfusion*, 50(6), 1257–1264. https://doi.org/10.1111/j.1537-2995.2009.02574.x.

Gilchrist, P.T., McGovern, G.E., Bekkouche, N., Bacon, S.L., & Ditto, B. (2015). The vasovagal response during confrontation with blood-injury-injection stimuli: the role of perceived control. *Journal of Anxiety Disorders*, 31, 43–48.

Jiang, M. Y., Upton, E., & Newby, J.M. (2020). A randomised wait-list controlled pilot trial of one-session virtual reality exposure therapy for blood-injection-injury phobias. *Journal of Affective Disorders*, 276, 636–645.

Marchiondo, K.J. (2010). Recognizing and treating vasovagal syncope. *American Journal of Nursing*, 110(4), 50-53. https://doi.org/10.1097/01.NAJ.0000370159.10352.a6.

McMurtry, C.M., Taddio, A., Noel, M., Antony, M.M., Chambers, C.T., Asmundson, G.J.G., & Scott, J. (2016). Exposure-based interventions for the management of individuals with high levels of needle fear across the lifespan: a clinical practice guideline and call for further research. *Cognitive Behaviour Therapy*, 45(3), 217–235. https:. https://doi.org/10.1080/16506073.2016.1157204.

Mednick, L.M., & Claar, R.L. (2012). Treatment of severe blood-injection-injury phobia with the applied-tension method: two adolescent case examples. *Clinical Case Studies*, 11(1), 24–34.

Sánchez-Navarro, J.P., Martínez-Selva, J.M., Maldonado, E.F., Carrillo-Verdejo, E., Pineda, S., & Torrente, G. (2018). Autonomic reactivity in blood-injection-injury and snake phobia. *Journal of Psychosomatic Research*, 115, 117–124.

Gold Standard Quote

https://onlinelibrary.wiley.com/doi/pdf/10.1002/da.22616?-casa_token=WVaLNYergr0AAAAA:ouk2TIWOQDvAzz-p_4L_duudSF7kBR95i2IymbkwzH5NTAdUmO3jEIf6KKn0BG-ztLTluO3DGQZ2BBEA.

CHAPTER 4

SELF-HYPNOSIS

THE WORD "HYPNOSIS" evokes images of stage hypnotists engaging in subtle psychological trickery to manipulate innocent audience members into doing foolish things beyond their control. Tales are told of hypnotized individuals remaining entranced for years.

However, hypnosis is a natural phenomenon that we experience daily. It is as natural as breathing. Have you ever passed your exit while driving, almost as if you were on autopilot? Have you daydreamed before? If you answered "yes" to any of these questions, then you have experienced hypnosis. Hypnosis is so natural that we are often unaware of its occurrence. In this chapter, you will learn how to harness this natural state to ease your phobia regarding needles, injections, and vaccines.

Hypnosis is a proven method to help you achieve important life goals and use your mental capabilities to better manage any challenges you encounter. These include:

- anxiety
- pain
- bad habits

Hypnosis exists along a continuum. Most people can be hypnotized to some degree. Hypnosis can be accessed in two ways: (1) via consultations with a trained hypnotherapist, or (2) by learning self-hypnosis.

WHAT IS SELF-HYPNOSIS?

Self-hypnosis is hypnosis that is deliberately created using your intention, attention, concentration, conviction, and full control. It is a technique used to create a desired change in your thoughts, feelings, and behaviors. You decide when it begins, its duration, and when it ends. We'll begin by learning how to hypnotize ourselves and craft our own self-hypnosis script to ease fears and anxieties regarding vaccinations. When you craft your own suggestions, the experts term this "autosuggestion." You can rely on this portable tool even while you are receiving a vaccine.

TRANCE

Essentially, a trance is a heightened state of attention in which people are more susceptible to suggestion. If you have ever daydreamed or experienced flow, then you have experienced a trance. When entranced, time becomes distorted. You may find that you are "losing track of time."

HOW DOES HYPNOSIS WORK?

Hypnosis and being absorbed in a good movie are similar states. Hypnosis comprises two stages: (1) induction, and (2) suggestion. During the induction stage, you are encouraged to relax, visualize, and listen closely to the words of the hypnotist. Suggestion is the next stage. There are three types of suggestion:

- ideomotor (e.g., hand levitation, responding to questions with finger movements, etc.)
- challenge (e.g., "just try to lift your heavy arm, just try," etc.)
- perceptual/cognitive (e.g., hallucinations, amnesia, etc.)

WILL HYPNOSIS MAKE ME LOSE CONTROL?

No. This is a common myth. You are in control when being hypnotized by a hypnotherapist or during self-hypnosis. In fact, hypnosis and self-hypnosis enable you to exercise greater control over your thoughts, feelings, and actions. The truth is, if you do not allow yourself to be hypnotized, then you will not be. You are in full control.

CAN I LEARN SELF-HYPNOSIS?

Absolutely. Remember, you naturally fall into a "trance" nearly every day. Self-hypnosis is a learned skill that will be introduced here. There are four steps to self-hypnosis:

1. Design your self-hypnosis based upon your situation.
2. Enter the trance.
3. Focus your attention on a specific goal.
4. Emerge from the trance.

Each of these four steps will be explained below with an example related to needle phobia.

DESIGN YOUR SELF-HYPNOSIS ACCORDING TO YOUR SITUATION

Hypnosis begins with how you think. When we are not thinking positively about ourselves, we feel unwell. When we feel unwell, we do not perform optimally. We are off our game and predisposed to making relatively small events feel far worse and more frightening than the actual situation.

Hypnosis is like programming. You have been exposed to programming since you were born. We genuinely do become what we think about. You create your thoughts. Your goal is to learn how to program yourself.

Later in this chapter, you will learn how to write your own self-hypnosis script to ease any distress you may have about receiving a vaccine. Writing your own script gives you control, especially if you recall a traumatic situation regarding needles, syringes, or vaccines that you directly experienced or witnessed. Let us continue to the second step in the four-step self-hypnosis process.

ENTER A TRANCE

Trance and induction refer to the same phenomenon. A popular way to deliberately hypnotize yourself is via the "eye induction method." Below are instructions on how to hypnotize yourself using this method:

> *Focus your attention on a spot on the ceiling. Try not to bend your neck backward; instead, move only your eyes to look up. Once your eyes have settled in place, focus your attention on the spot. Do not move your eyes. Stay focused on the spot. Now, take a deep breath. Keep concentrating on the spot. Notice that it may be increasingly difficult to focus on the spot. The more you try to concentrate, the more your eyes may feel as if they are becoming tired or heavy. Keeping your eyes focused on the spot...notice the heaviness in your eyes...your eyes blinking...yes...blinking. Close your eyes and simply relax as best as you can.*

FOCUS YOUR ATTENTION ON A SPECIFIC GOAL

Focusing your attention on a specific goal first requires you to ask yourself, "What would be the ideal experience for me when getting an injection or vaccine?" Be sure to record your responses using the autosuggestion script form below.

My Ideal Needle or Vaccine Experience: Autosuggestion Script Form

I am physically feeling _____.

I am emotionally feeling _____.

I am thinking that _____.

I know for sure that _____.

I tell myself that the benefits are _____.

Even if I feel a bit uncomfortable, I know I can _____.

After completing this form, remember the key words and phrases that enable you to feel more in control and master your feelings, thoughts, sensations, and other experiences.

As you create your own script of suggestions, you can have more general autosuggestions, such as:

> *"I see myself as successfully getting vaccinated with more ease than ever before."*

Or you can have more detailed autosuggestions, such as:

> *"I imagine myself practicing the applied tension technique in the car before going to my vaccine appointment. I see myself breathing a relaxing sigh of relief after signing up for the vaccine. As I await my turn, I notice some tight physical sensations, but I know how to smooth out these kinks by tensing and relaxing. I know that this experience lasts seconds, while the long-term benefits may last a lifetime. Upon being called, I visualize myself as being in control of my experience. I know that I can tolerate getting the vaccine*

because I have portable tools that I can use at any time. Upon feeling the swipe of the alcohol, I tense and relax my muscles while selecting a point in the room to focus on or choose to close my eyes and imagine a relaxing or funny scene. I feel the prick and remind myself that it is simply a bit of pain in a miniscule part of my entire body. I feel the bandage on my arm, and I imagine myself as a champion who has beaten the odds, and I feel not good, but great about what I just accomplished. With full confidence, I proudly leave the venue, knowing and feeling that I did the right thing for myself and for society."

You will notice that these suggestions are written in the present tense. For example, "I know that I can tolerate the pain" instead of "I will be able to tolerate the pain." It is crucial to write the script for the present moment, thus, in the present tense instead of the future tense.

More helpful tips for writing your script:

As you write your first script, it may be helpful to remember the difference between direct and indirect suggestions. You may also use the following phrases to begin each sentence in your script:

- "Imagine this…"
- "Picture this…"
- "See yourself…"
- "See what happens when…"
- "Visualize that…"

Finally, ensure that your script does not contain negative words, such as "will not." You want to write your script to capture only positivity. For instance, there is a difference between, "I will not feel any nervousness about getting an injection" and "When I anticipate getting an injection, I know that there are portable tools I can use to calm and center myself."

RECORDING MY SELF-HYPNOSIS SCRIPT

You may record the script that you created, then simply play the recording. You can download a variety of recording apps for your smart device. If you do not have access to such technologies, you could use a cassette recorder, a telephone answering machine, or a CD on your computer.

EMERGING FROM THE TRANCE

Coming out of a trance is as important as allowing yourself to enter a trance. To come out of trance is to reorient or re-alert. As you emerge from the trance, incorporate the "Four R's," as described below:

- Return – This involves reorienting to a state of full alertness and awareness.
- Remember – This is a cue to remember what you said to yourself and what you experienced that is positively memorable.
- Refresh – This is a cue to connect with that which was refreshing, re-energizing, and relaxing.
- Remove – This is a cue to accept all suggestions that were helpful and release any thoughts and feelings that were unhelpful.

There are several ways to come out of a trance and reorient. The method below offers simple and effective instructions to reorient.

After focusing on all the steps leading up to a successful vaccination, I tell myself that it is time to return to full awareness. As I become more alert, I recall the wonderful experience of protecting myself and those I love by getting vaccinated with greater ease than ever.

Reflecting on the wonderfully calming experience I created for myself, I am listening for five things I hear. Now, I am opening my eyes and looking around the room, naming five things I can see. I stretch, gently feeling increasingly awake and alert. I rub my hands together. Next, I count backward from fifty-seven in threes. Finally, I spell my last name backward.

HOW DO I ADVANCE MY SELF-HYPNOSIS SKILLS?

To become more skilled at self-hypnosis, consider following these six recommendations developed by the United Kingdom's National Health Service (NHS):

- Commit to practicing self-hypnosis.
- Consider the anxiety or pain you experience.
- Try self-hypnosis when the pain is mild.
- Trust that with practice, the benefits of self-hypnosis for pain reduction last longer.
- Experiment to see what works best for you.
- Reward yourself for trying, experimenting, and practicing self-hypnosis.

HIGHLIGHTS TO RECALL

Many concepts are presented in this chapter on self-hypnosis. Below are a few key highlights for you to remember how to enhance your ability to use self-hypnosis as a portable tool before or during a vaccine or injection:

- Self-hypnosis leverages a natural and normal state.
- Self-hypnosis narrows your attention, focus, and concentration.
- It is often accompanied by a feeling of relaxation and calm.
- Self-hypnosis with intentionality (i.e., creating your own self-hypnosis script) is easily learned because it is a natural state that occurs throughout the day.

You have added the portable tool of self-hypnosis to your toolkit. Ensure that you take the personally crafted self-hypnosis script with you and be ready to use it when needed. To maximize its usefulness, incorporate self-hypnosis into your daily routine to ease the fears, anxieties, and phobias that may appear throughout the day.

Next, we'll turn our attention to a topic that you may find amusing or even embarrassing—talking to yourself. Chapter 6 does not teach you how to talk to yourself, but it does guide you through shaping your self-talk to serve as a support and resource. Now, it is time to learn how to fully leverage your self-talk to benefit you in many situations, including getting vaccinated or receiving an injection.

TIPS FOR EDUCATORS, HEALTHCARE PROFESSIONALS, AND THERAPISTS

There are various types of hypnotherapy (Alladin, 2016). Cognitive hypnotherapy (CH) is listed among the "third wave" therapies, along with mindfulness, in the treatment of anxiety (Alladin, 2014). Below are tips for utilizing hypnotherapy in the treatment of needle and injection phobias:

- Offer hypnosis as a treatment option for the client or patient by suggesting, "One of the options we can offer you today to keep you comfortable during the vaccination is hypnosis."
- Explain to clients or patients that a trance is natural and normal and that hypnosis refers to the process of inducing a trance and utilizing suggestions to achieve a goal. Furthermore, hypnotherapy is the use of hypnosis to achieve clinical goals and treatment outcomes.
- Consider replacing hypnosis with relaxation training when rendering systematic desensitization in the treatment of specific phobias for clients or patients who cannot tolerate exposure therapy (Iglesias & Iglesias, 2013).
- Combine hypnosis with cognitive behavioral therapy (CBT), given the empirical evidence demonstrating the benefits of both these therapies in the treatment of acute stress disorder (Bryant et al., 2005).
- Educate and encourage clients or patients to engage in self-hypnosis, given the empirical evidence suggesting its effectiveness among healthy volunteers (VandeVusse et al., 2010) in decreasing baseline anxiety.

In closing, remember that while hypnosis and relaxation techniques may seem similar, they are not.

REFERENCES

Alladin, A. (2014). The wounded self: New approach to understanding and treating anxiety disorders. *American Journal of Clinical Hypnosis*, 56(4), 368–388. doi:10.1080/00029157.2014.880045.

Alladin, A. (2016). Cognitive hypnotherapy for accessing and healing emotional injuries in anxiety disorders. *American Journal of Clinical Hypnosis*, 59(1), 24–46. doi:10.1080/00029157.2016.1163662.

Bryant, R. A., Moulds, M. L., Guthrie, R. M., & Nixon, R. D. (2005). The additive benefit of hypnosis and cognitive-behavioral therapy in treating acute stress disorder. *Journal of Consulting and Clinical Psychology*, 73(2), 334–340. doi:10.1037/0022-006X.73.2.334.

Iglesias, A., & Iglesias, A. (2013). I-95 Phobia treated with hypnotic systematic desensitization: A case report. *American Journal of Clinical Hypnosis*, 56(2), 143–151. doi:10.1080/00029157.2013.785930.

VandeVusse, L., Hanson, L., Berner, M. A., Winters J. M. (2010). Impact of self-hypnosis in women on select physiologic and psychological parameters. *Journal of Obstetric, Gynecologic, and Neonatal Nursing*, 39(2), 159–168. doi:10.1111/j.1552-6909.2010.01103.x.

CHAPTER 5

EXPOSURE THERAPY

HAVE YOU HEARD the saying "Feel the fear and do it anyway"? This statement captures the essence of exposure therapy. In exposure therapy, however, it is not as simple as just "doing it anyway." This is because you decide how fast or slow you want to expose yourself to that which you fear, avoid, or simply get freaked out by.

Exposure therapy is an evidence-based technique used by therapists to treat all types of anxiety disorders, including phobias, and it has been proven to effectively treat people with needle phobias. This chapter will provide you with a step-by-step process to systematically confront your fear of needles, injections, and vaccines with the goal of decreasing your fearful reaction.

There are five reasons why learning this technique is important for you as you seek to conquer your phobia of needles, injections, shots, or vaccines:

- It helps you face what you have been avoiding.
- It lessens your anxiety over time.
- It helps you learn portable skills to better handle your fear or phobia.
- It gives you greater control in your life.
- It protects yourself and others by helping you get vaccinated.

After reading chapter 5, you will be able to apply the steps of the single most effective technique available to conquer most phobias, including needle and injection phobia. To overcome your phobia, you will begin by listing your fears, from least to most intense. Then, you will apply some of the techniques you learned in chapters 3 and chapter 4 to move yourself from the stage of avoidance to the stage of approach.

PACING OF EXPOSURE THERAPY

There are three ways in which exposure therapy can be paced, ranging from gradual to rapid approach. Each of these methods is described below.

- Graded exposure: With graded exposure therapy, you will be exposed to a situation or stimulus that triggers your fear or phobia related to needles and vaccines. Over time, you will be exposed to situations or stimuli that produce more fears, to the point that your feelings of fear, anxiety, and distress will decrease.
- Systematic desensitization: With systematic desensitization, you gradually face stimuli or situations that cause anxiety. The underlying premise of systematic desensitization is that

you cannot be relaxed and fearful or anxious at the same time (Corah, Gale, & Illig, 1979).

- Flooding: With flooding, you will be immediately exposed to the highest level of fear-producing stimuli. Unlike graded exposure and systematic desensitization, you are not exposed step-by-step. When you expose yourself in this way using imaginal stimuli, such as photos and videos, this is called "implosion."

This chapter will teach you the graded exposure method of exposure therapy. We do not recommend flooding as a self-help technique, as this is reserved for those working with a healthcare practitioner trained in flooding or implosion. Systematic desensitization as a technique will be covered in section 3 of this book.

SYSTEMATIC DESENSITIZATION

Systematic desensitization has three simple steps:

1. Relaxation training
2. Development of the anxiety hierarchy
3. Desensitization of anxiety by repeated pairing of imagined fear evoking stimuli with deep relaxation (Cormier & Nurius, 2003)

First, place yourself into a relaxing state, then imagine the stimuli that cause a small degree of fear. Second, relax again and then, once relaxed when imagining the feared stimuli, stop imagining it. Remember these steps then start all over again. Each time the stimuli are no longer strong enough, think of something more anxiety inducing.

ONE SESSION OR MULTIPLE SESSIONS

The scientific evidence shows that exposure therapy, performed as a single session lasting two to three hours or as multiple one-hour sessions with each session spread over time, works in treating needles fears or phobias (McCurty et al., 2015). You can see this man exposing himself to a photo of a needle on his laptop. He appears to be uncomfortable. This man should continue to look at this photo until his discomfort dissolves over time.

Evidence suggests that repeated exposure is an effective treatment for specific phobias (Ayala et al., 2009). Beyond the number of sessions of exposure therapy, research has shown that exposure is more effective if done in multiple settings instead of just in one setting (de Jong, Lommen, de Jong, & Nauta, 2019).

MEASURING YOUR DISTRESS

Distress is measured on a scale from 0 to 10, with 0 meaning no distress, 5 meaning moderate distress, and 10 meaning the worst distress one can possibly imagine.

CONSTRUCTION OF FEAR HIERARCHY (FEAR LADDER)

Regardless of the pace and the number of sessions, the first step in exposure therapy (not including flooding) is to construct your fear hierarchy. This is also called a fear ladder. Before you learn how to construct your own fear hierarchy, there are three benefits to investing your time and energy in constructing your hierarchy. By constructing your fear hierarchy you:

- express them by putting them on paper rather than having those fears constantly swirling in your head;
- analyze the situation with greater specificity to target what is triggering your fear at an unbelievably detailed and granular level; and
- you now have a greater understanding of how you experience needle fear or phobia.

Now that you are familiar with the three benefits of constructing your fear hierarchy, you are ready to begin constructing your hierarchy of fears or phobias of needles. The instructions are below.

STEP-BY-STEP INSTRUCTIONS ON HOW TO CONSTRUCT YOUR FEAR HIERARCHY

1. Reflect on the entire experience—from making an appointment, to getting a vaccine, to leaving the site after getting the shot. Then, write down as many situations as possible related to this entire experience, in as much detail as possible.

2. Arrange these situations in order from least distressing to the most distressing by thinking about each situation and imagining or recalling just how bad it would be to be in that situation.

3. Create your hierarchy by including about ten to twenty situations or items, beginning with items that are so mild that they hardly trigger any fear or anxiety at all.

The outcome of taking these three steps is that you now have a ranked list of anxiety-evoking items organized in a hierarchy that you will now use for the next step. Look at the sample hierarchy to get a sense of how your hierarchy should be organized. The next step is to put your fear hierarchy into action.

Table 4: Sample Hierarchy

Step	Stimuli/Situation	Fear Rating
10		
9	Getting a shot in the upper arm	
8	Slightly pricking one's skin with a needle	
7	Watching someone else get a needle	
6	Resting the needle against the vein	
5	Rubbing an alcohol swab against one's skin	
4	Holding a needle	
3	Observing somebody getting a vaccine at the site	
2	Waiting at the site to get vaccinated	
1	Looking at a picture of a needle	2

PUTTING YOUR CONSTRUCTED FEAR HIERARCHY INTO ACTION

Look at your constructed fear hierarchy. Select the least distressing situation in the hierarchy. As you imagine or engage in this behavior, ask yourself, "What is my level of distress from 0 to 10?" If 0 or 1, then congratulate yourself first before moving up to the next rung in the ladder. Then, do it again and again. Why? Because the key to making exposure therapy work is repeated exposure to situations or stimuli that are distressing along the continuum from 0 to 10.

You can see how the level of distress associated with the needle in the hands of the nurse is a 9 but the level of distress kicks up to 10 when the needle is inserted in the arm.

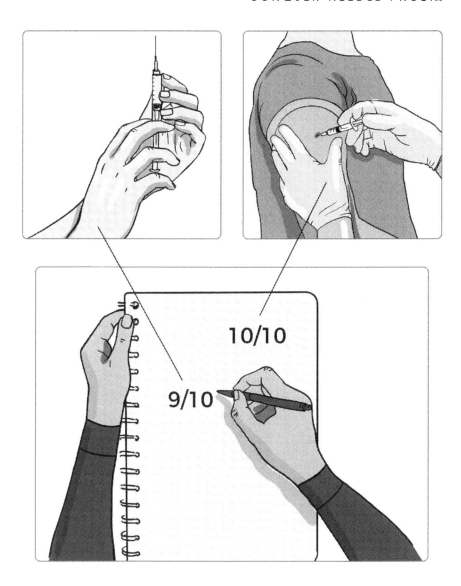

Remember, the key to exposure therapy is to continue to expose yourself to that which is causing you distress until the 9 decreases to 2–4 and the 10 drops to 2–4. This may take time. This may take one exposure or multiple exposures.

EXPOSURE THERAPY PLUS

Exposure therapy is effective in treating phobias of needles and injections (McMurty et al., 2015). Research has shown that to really get a treatment boost, you should add the ATT technique that you learned in chapter 3.

HIGHLIGHTS TO RECALL

This chapter exposed you to a robust and powerful technique to help lessen the suffering associated with phobias of needles and injection. You can also apply the lessons you learned in this chapter to phobias and extreme fears of other situations or objects.

Below are a few key highlights for you to solidify your application of exposure therapy and solidify the gains made thus far to conquer your phobias related to needles and injections.

- Encourage yourself to systematically confront your fears.
- Break down, in minute-by-minute detail, what makes you fearful—from barely fearful at all to so fearful that you avoid the situation or object completely.
- Escalate yourself gently and compassionately to confront each fear by progressing from one fear-inducing stimulus to another.
- Reward yourself with each rung of the fear ladder that you climb.
- Remember that you are in control and that phobias can be controlled.
- Remember to boost this technique by adding ATT.

The next technique you will learn is based on a natural act that you do every minute of the day— positive self talk. In fact, you can use the technique while you are getting a vaccine, shot, or blood draw. Chapter 6 in Section II shows you how to optimize self-talk to enhance your coping skills on the spot.

TIPS FOR EDUCATORS, HEALTHCARE PROFESSIONALS, AND THERAPISTS

Exposure therapy is regarded as a first-line treatment for specific phobias (Barlow et al., 2015; Chambless et al., 1998; Steinman et al., 2015).

- Use exposure therapy as the sole treatment and provide robust evidence for such use (Wechsler, Kümpers, & Mühlberger, 2019).
- Decide which type of exposure therapy you will use: imaginal (exposure *in sensu*), live (exposure *in vivo*), or VRET (exposure *in virtuo*).
- Decide whether you will use gradual exposure therapy or flooding.
- Stay up to date on the literature regarding VRET. Current research suggests that a single-session VRET for needle phobia results in changes in thoughts and reduces fear to some degree, yet the evidence is not convincing enough to suggest that VRET should be used as a stand-alone treatment (Jiang, Upton, & Newby, 2020).

REFERENCES

Ayala, E. S., Meuret, A. E., & Ritz, T. (2009). Treatments for blood-injury-injection phobia: A critical review of current evidence. *Journal of Psychiatric Research*, 43, 1235-1242.

Barlow, D. H., Conklin, L. R., & Bentley, K. H. (2015). Psychological treatments for panic disorders, phobias, and social and generalized anxiety disorders. In P. E. Nathan & J. M. Gorman (Eds.), A guide to treatments that work (4th ed., pp. 409–462). Oxford University Press. https://doi.org/10.1093/med:psych/9780199342211.003.0014.

Chambless, D. L., Baker-Ericzen, M., Baucom, D., Beutler, L. E., Calhoun, K. S., Crits-Christoph, P., Daiuto, A., DeRubeis, R., Detweiler, J., Haaga, D. A. F., Bennett Johnson, S., McCurry, S., Mueser, K. T., Pope, K. S., Sanderson, W. C., Shoham, V., Stickle, T., Williams, D. A., & Woody, S. R. (1998). Update on empirically validated therapies, II. *Clinical Psychologist*, 51, 3-16. https://doi.org/10.1037/e619622010-001.

Corah, N. L., Gale, E. N. & Illig, S. J. (1979). Psychological stress reduction during dental procedures *Journal of Dental Research*, 58, 1347-1351.

Cormier, S. & Nurius, P. O. 2003. Interview and change strategies for helpers: fundamental skills and cognitive behavioral intervention (5th ed.). Pacific Grove, CA: Brooks/Cole

de Jong, R., Lommen, M. J. J., de Jong, P. J., & Nauta, M. H. (2019). Using multiple contexts and retrieval cues in exposure-based therapy to prevent relapse in anxiety disorders. *Cognitive and Behavioral Practice*, 26, 154-165.

Jiang, M. Y. W., Upton, E., Newby, J. M. (2020). A randomized wait-list controlled pilot trial of one-session VR exposure therapy for blood-injection-injury phobias. *Journal of Affective Disorders*, 276, 636-645.

McMurty et al. (2015) Interventions for individuals with high levels of needle fear: Systematic review of randomized controlled trials and quasi-randomized controlled trials. *Clinical Journal of Pain*, 31, S109-S123.

Steinman, S. A., Wootton, B. M., Tolin, D. F. (2015). Exposure therapy for anxiety disorders In H. S. Friedman (Ed.), Encyclopedia of Mental Health. Elsevier (pp. 186-191).

Wechsler, T. F., Kümpers, F. & Mühlberger, A. (2019). Inferiority or even superiority of virtual reality exposure therapy in phobias? —A systematic review and quantitative meta-analysis on randomized controlled trials specifically comparing the efficacy of virtual reality exposure to gold standard in vivo exposure in agoraphobia, specific phobia, and social phobia. *Frontiers in Psychology*, 10, 1758.

SECTION II

TOOLS TO USE DURING YOUR APPOINTMENT

CHAPTER 6

SELF-TALK

AFTER YOU LEARN to use self-hypnosis, apply the ATT technique, and practice exposure therapy, it is the right time to start developing positive self-talk skills as well. Without these skills, you are likely to engage in negative self-talk. Negative self-talk will cause you to experience more fear, anxiety, and phobia, as well as a lack of control. By the end of this chapter, you will be equipped to achieve the following:

Insights

- Appreciate self-talk and its connection with and needle fear and phobia
- Understand the history behind your self-talk

Strategies

- Identify patterns in your self-talk
- Catch your negative self-talk before it goes too far
- Change your self-talk from negative to positive

Deliberate practice and mindful and consistent application of these two insights and three strategies will yield benefits beyond addressing fears and phobias related to needles, vaccines, and injections. Now, it is time to try a thought experiment.

THOUGHT EXPERIMENT: THE POWER OF SELF-TALK

Picture yourself waiting in traffic because of an automobile accident on the road. There is no other route. You need to arrive at your destination in fifteen minutes and, under normal circumstances, you would be able to get there in ten minutes. While waiting in the traffic jam, you say the following to yourself:

- Why did I take this route?
- I should have realized that I needed to leave earlier.
- If I am late, so-and-so will never forgive me.
- I am so stupid for making this mistake.
- I cannot take this.
- Of all the days, why now? Why today?

In the space below, describe how you would feel if any of these thoughts were to keep running in your mind while you were waiting in the traffic jam.

Now, imagine that you can hear the self-talk of another person right beside you who is stuck in the same traffic jam. The following thoughts run through their mind:

- Let me call so-and-so to let them know that I might be late.
- It may be a good time to think about this upcoming project because the traffic is not moving.
- I'll change the radio to a more upbeat or relaxing station.
- I know that, if I get worked up, I can take a few deep breaths to calm down.
- Let me at least get comfortable and stretch every now and then since the traffic is at a standstill.

In the space below, describe how you would feel if any of these thoughts were to run through your mind while you were waiting in the traffic jam.

You have probably described quite different feelings in the two boxes. However, both you and the other person are stuck in the same traffic jam, yet their perceptions of the situation are quite different. Why? Your self-talk or internal monologue shapes your perceptions. Your self-talk emerges spontaneously, almost automatically. It is as if you do not even realize it until after you have already experienced the thought and then feel a rush of emotions and physical sensations, ranging from delight to fear.

The bottom line is that our interpretations and thoughts regarding what is happening, rather than the situation itself, drive our feelings (e.g., the traffic jam). This sequence is depicted in the following flowchart.

In summary, you are largely responsible for how you feel—unless your feelings stem from certain medical conditions or extreme situations beyond your control. It may be a bit difficult to accept this fact. Many of us tend to blame others or external events rather than ourselves or our interpretations of situations.

THE STORY OF VICTOR E. FRANKL: LESSONS FOR ALL OF US

Victor E. Frankl authored the famed book *Man's Search for Meaning.* He survived living in Nazi concentration camps from 1942 to 1945 under intolerable and cruel conditions. His father, mother, brother, and wife died in these camps. Trained as a psychiatrist, he helped other inmates resist suicide by teaching them to focus on and remember that which is good, healthy, and positive. Victor E. Frankl captured what he learned during these three horrific years in the passage below.

> "Between stimulus and response there is a space. In that space is our power to choose our response. In our response lies our growth and our freedom."

This quote is a reminder to me, and hopefully to you, that we have the freedom to choose our response. Both you and I are the products of our thoughts, not our conditions.

SELF-TALK AND ITS CONNECTION TO FEAR AND PHOBIA

Self-talk can work either for you or against you. Psychologists refer to self-talk that advances a healthier, better attitude as positive self-talk. In contrast, self-talk that belittles, stresses, and restrains you is negative self-talk. The way you think about situations and events, such as getting an injection, influences how you feel about them. Based on your thoughts, you might feel bad or even avoid the situation altogether if you think that it will be too overwhelming for you to handle. In chapter 2, you read that the hallmark sign of any phobia is avoidance. In the case of immunization, blood draws, and medical and dental procedures, avoidance can render you and others very vulnerable. People with phobias and with various types of anxiety engage in more negative self-talk than others.

UNDERSTAND THE HISTORY
BEHIND YOUR SELF-TALK

We create stories about our lives. It begins in childhood, when we weave our perceptions of ourselves and the world around us into a narrative about what we can and will do. These stories are called "life scripts" or "cognitive schemas."

These life scripts continue to have a deep and an unconscious effect on how we live our lives. They affect the decisions that we make. They control what we believe we can easily do and can never do. They shape our self-image. Yet, we seldom realize where they come from or that they exist in the first place.

You may have developed life scripts early in life based on the negative or positive influences that shaped you as a child or an adolescent. Your life scripts are shaped by your parents, relatives, and other influential figures during your early years. In this manner, you become a product of your family history, to some degree. In addition to your family, your culture and national sentiments also shape your life scripts.

Life scripts are expressed very clearly (e.g., "I'm not the type of person who can withstand anything uncomfortable"). Life scripts can either be incredibly detailed or vague. Further, they can be very empowering or imprisoning. In a study comparing phobic and nonphobic individuals (Wenzel & Holt, 2000), it was found that all phobic individuals had an increased heart rate when exposed to threatening stimuli. Furthermore, those with blood or injury phobias felt nervous, felt scared, or screamed.

Our life scripts are also called cognitive schemas by psychologists. They are adapted from a particular situation and a specific time, but they may have outlived their usefulness for other situations and times. Schemas allow us to rapidly determine what is happening at a given moment without thinking too much about the details of the situation (Lim et al., 2020). In short, a cognitive schema is similar to a prediction.

A prediction is an image of the future that is based on past experience and knowledge (Lim et al., 2020). With regard to pain, some of us are more likely to catastrophize (Elman & Borsook, 2018). Others who are more aware or mindful of their body may be able to mitigate the influence of negative cognitive schemas and reduce persistent pain (Harrison et al., 2019). In chapter 8, you will learn more about the power of mindfulness in improving your perception of pain and alleviating fear and anxiety. The good news is that you can modify your cognitive schemas. You will learn how to do so shortly.

IDENTIFY PATTERNS IN YOUR SELF-TALK

The best way to identify patterns in your self-talk is to pause and reflect on any common themes underlying your self-talk.

- Do I perceive the glass as half-full or half-empty?
- Do I remember uplifting or distressing or depressing events more easily?
- Do I motivate myself to move forward, drag myself down, or amp myself up?
- Do I engage in the same self-talk across all situations and under all circumstances?
- Does my self-talk change when I am around different people?

Reflect upon these five questions. If you responded, "half-empty," "distressing or disturbing," "drag myself down," and "amp myself up," then this pattern of self-talk will not help you when you face a challenging situation such as getting vaccinated or going to the dentist to get an injection. If you discover that your self-talk is positive or that it is negative because of the situation or the people around you, or both, then this is good news.

Do not despair if you do not like your responses. Why? Because you can change the way you think and your self-talk patterns. You are not your pattern. Let us continue to learn how to add more positive, healthy, and adaptive self-talk skills to your portable toolkit.

THOUGHT DIARY WORKSHEET TOOL

In the Thought Diary Worksheet, you will find a dedicated space for you to describe the situation you are facing (e.g., getting vaccinated). Write down your primary thought about getting the vaccine (e.g., "No big deal" or "I can't deal with this"). Next, rate the extent to which you experience this thought. The rating can range from 0 percent (not at all) to 100 percent (all the way). Now, move on to the other side of the worksheet and write down the emotion or feeling that you are experiencing (e.g., confident or anxious). Then, rate the intensity of the feeling that you have written down. It can range from 0 percent (not at all) to 100 percent (all the way). Reflect for a moment and ask yourself the following questions:

- Do I see a connection between my thoughts and emotions about the situation?
- If I change my thoughts about this situation, will I also feel differently? Is this possible?

Picture yourself as a gentle attorney cross-examining a witness on the witness stand in a court of law. You turn to the witness and ask, "What evidence do you have for your thoughts about the situation?" Now, ask yourself the same question about your thoughts about the situation you have written down and note them down under "Evidence For."

Next, imagine yourself as a journalist. Journalists are supposed to be objective and provide balanced reports. A journalist would ask for contrary evidence supporting the other side of the story. Accordingly, ask yourself the following question: "What evidence do I have that my thoughts about the situation are incorrect?" You have now argued both sides. You have found evidence that supports your thoughts about the situation as well as evidence that challenges your thoughts about the situation. This process is called "seeking contrary evidence."

Now, it is time to find alternative thoughts that will lower your level of distress about the situation and help you tolerate it, if not master it. Write down your alternative thought about the situation. For example, your original, automatic, or learned thought may have been "I can't do this" but your alternative thought may be "It is hard, but I can tolerate this." After writing down your alternative thought, rate how strongly you believe the alternative thought. It can range from 0 percent (not at all) to 100 percent (all the way). Next, write down the emotions elicited by your alternative thought (not your original thought). How intense are the emotions elicited by the alternative thought? Rate them on a scale ranging from 0 percent (not at all intense) to 100 percent (extremely intense).

Thought Diary Worksheet

SITUATION	
THOUGHT	**EMOTION**
BELIEF IN THOUGHT (0-100%)	**INTENSITY OF EMOTION (0-100%)**
EVIDENCE FOR	**EVIDENCE AGAINST**
ALTERNATIVE THOUGHT	**EMOTION**
BELIEF IN ALTERNATIVE THOUGHT (0-100%)	**INTENSITY OF EMOTION (0-100%)**

CATCH YOUR NEGATIVE SELF-TALK BEFORE IT GOES TOO FAR

Watch out for the "what ifs." Anxiety can be induced almost instantly by repeating any phrase that begins with the two words "what if." For instance, when contemplating scheduling a vaccination, you may ask yourself, "What if the needle really, really hurts?" or you may ask,

"What if I can't handle the pain?" Just noticing when you fall into the "what if" thinking trap is the first step toward gaining control over your negative self-talk. Positive change occurs when you begin to counter and replace negative "what if" statements with positive, self-supportive statements that bolster your ability to cope effectively. The Thought Diary Worksheet above will help you record your negative self-talk about specific situations.

CHANGE YOUR SELF-TALK FROM
NEGATIVE TO POSITIVE

The most effective way to deal with negative self-talk is to counter it with positive and supportive statements. For example, you might say, "So what," "These are just thoughts," "I can handle this," "This is worth it because it will protect me and my family," "I've done this before," or "I can breathe, let go, and relax."

Countering negative self-talk requires you to write down and rehearse positive statements that directly disprove or refute that negative self-talk. The Thought Diary Worksheet above walks you through this process; you can use this tool to write down evidence against your original thought.

If you experience anxiety because of negative mental programming, you can begin to change the way you feel by replacing it with positive programming. The Thought Diary Worksheet will help you construct an adaptive thought that can replace your original one.

HIGHLIGHTS TO RECALL

· ·

This chapter informed you about the power of your self-talk, internal dialog, and life scripts or cognitive schemas. Now, you should know that your thinking influences your emotions substantially. If you cope with a situation by engaging in positive self-talk, you are likely to feel less anxious and stressed and more in control. However, if you cope with a situation by engaging in negative self-talk, you will experience negative emotions. In short, knowing that you have to get your blood drawn is a threatening situation. Two people can experience different emotions about this impending event. How is this possible? They may view the situation differently and respond to it differently because of differences in their self-talk.

The following are a few key highlights for you to reflect upon as you move one step closer to conquering your fear or phobia related to needles and injections.

- Identify patterns in your self-talk.
- Catch your negative self-talk before it goes too far.
- Change your self-talk from negative to positive.
- Use the Thought Diary Worksheet.

The next technique that you will learn is based on a natural activity in which you engage every minute of the day: distraction. Chapter 7 focuses on distraction. Distraction is something that often happens naturally. Let us learn how to optimize natural distraction and transform it into a powerful tool to conquer your fear or phobia of needles.

TIPS FOR EDUCATORS, HEALTHCARE PROFESSIONALS, AND THERAPISTS

After reading this chapter on self-talk, it must be evident that this is about cognitive restructuring. The main reason for including cognitive restructuring—which is one of the tools in cognitive behavior therapy (CBT)—is that it works. Cognitive restructuring is similar to cognitive reappraisal in that patients or clients reinterpret negative stimuli. In fact, there is a substantial body of evidence demonstrating the efficacy of CBT in treating anxiety disorders (Carpenter et al., 2019) and blood-injury-injection (BII) phobia (Craske, Antony & Barlow, 2006). In one study involving the use of manualized treatment for BII phobia, cognitive restructuring was included in the multicomponent treatment package (Chapman & DeLapp, 2014). In the same study, the adult patient responded to the multicomponent manualized CBT treatment, which included cognitive restructuring. As you know, each patient or client does not respond in the same way. There were individual differences between the groups.

The theoretical basis of cognitive restructuring as a tool for individuals with fears or phobias of needles is that exaggerated and negative predictions (self-talk) about what may happen during exposure to a feared situation are the hallmarks of anxiety disorders (Clark, 1999).

For further reading about cognitive restructuring, refer to the article published by Clark (2014), who has outlined twelve verbal intervention strategies that can be employed in cognitive restructuring. A few of these haven been highlighted and described in this chapter. These include evidence gathering, consequential analysis, generation of alternatives, and reframing or perspective taking.

REFERENCES

Carpenter, J. K., Pinaire, M., & Hofmann, S. G. (2019). From extinction learning to anxiety treatment: Mind the gap. *Brain Sciences,* 9(7), 164. https://doi.org/10.3390/brainsci9070164

Chapman, L. K. & DeLapp, R. C. T. (2014). Nine session treatment of a blood-injection-injury phobia with manualized cognitive behavioral therapy: An adult case example. *Clinical Case Studies*, 13(4), 299–312. https://doi.org/10.1177/1534650113509304

Clark, D. A. (2014). Cognitive restructuring. In The Wiley Handbook of Cognitive Behavior Therapy, 1st ed. Edited by Stefan G. Hoffman. New York, NY: John Wiley and Sons.

Clark, D. M. (1999). Anxiety disorders: Why they persist and how to treat them. *Behaviour Research and Therapy*, 37(1), S5–27. https://doi.org/10.1016/S0005-7967(99)00048-0

Craske, M. G., Antony, M. M., & Barlow, D. H. (2006). Mastering your Fears and Phobias: Therapist Guide, 2nd ed. New York, NY: Oxford University Press.

Elman, I., & Borsook, D. (2018). Threat response system: Parallel brain processes in pain vis- à-vis fear and anxiety. *Frontiers in Psychiatry*, 9, 29. https://doi.org/10.3389/fpsyt.2018.00029

Harrison, R., Zeidan, F., Kitsaras, G., Ozcelik, D., & Salomons, T. V. (2019). Trait mindfulness is associated with lower pain reactivity and connectivity of the default mode network. *Journal of Pain*, 20(6), 645–654. https://doi.org/10.1016/j.jpain.2018.10.011

Lim, M., O'Grady, C., Cane, D., Goyal, A., Lynch, M., Beyea, S., & Hashmi, J. A. (2020). Threat prediction from schemas as a source of bias in pain perception. *Journal of Neuroscience: The Official Journal of the Society for Neuroscience*, 40(7), 1538–1548. https://doi.org/10.1523/JNEUROSCI.2104-19.2019

Shrestha, S. & Stanley, M. (2020). Self-help workbook: Calming tools to manage anxiety. South Central Veterans Affairs Mental Illnesses Research and Clinical Centers. Available at: https://www.va.gov/HOMELESS/nchav/resources/docs/veteran-populations/aging/Self-Help-STOP-Worry-A-Tool-for-Older-Veterans-Self-Help-Workbook-508.pdf

Wenzel, A., & Holt, C. S. (2000). Situation-specific scripts for threat in two specific phobias. *Journal of Psychopathology and Behavioral Assessment*, 22(1), 1–21. https://doi.org/10.1023/A:1007585930209

CHAPTER 7

DISTRACTION

IF YOU ARE like most people, you have been taught to fight distraction. You have been taught to focus on the task at hand. In this chapter, you will learn that this doesn't have to apply to every situation. When faced with a distressing situation such as getting an injection, you may find comfort in watching every movement made by the vaccinator—from preparing to injecting the syringe. Alternatively, you may find comfort by purposefully focusing on anything but the needle. In short, you may find comfort in distracting yourself "by any means necessary" during an injection.

The first goal of this chapter is to help you make a case for using distraction as a tool to relieve your fear and anxiety while getting a shot. Then, this chapter will walk you through how distractions work to conquer needle phobia. This chapter will offer you more than ten ways in which you can distract yourself using all of your senses. Finally, it will guide you through the process of making sure that you take your go-to distraction tool with you the next time you get vaccinated or get an injection. After reading chapter 7, you will be able to not only add another tool to your portable toolkit, but you will also know when to use the tool and how it works for you and others.

THE CASE FOR DISTRACTION: IT'S MORE THAN COMMON SENSE—IT WORKS

Experienced healthcare practitioners and vaccinators are aware of ways to distract the patient from looking at the needle. They are particularly mindful if they sense any fear or anxiety from the patient. If they do, then—beginning with rubbing your arm with an alcohol swab until getting the needle out—they may ask you a question, talk to you, request that you look away, let you know that you can close your eyes if you wish, or even say, "You're doing great." This is especially true for children and adults. Distraction is an intentional shift of focus. It is a momentary but welcome escape.

There is solid scientific evidence on the efficacy of distraction, including a randomized controlled trial, which is the "gold standard" for scientists. One such study compared distraction techniques to a local anesthetic and it was concluded that distraction was more effective than local anesthetics in reducing pain perception during PVC (needle) insertion (Balanyuk et al., 2018, p. 55). Now that the case has been made that distraction works, it is time to learn how and why it works.

HOW DISTRACTION WORKS

. . . .

Distracting yourself requires little planning and effort on your part. Imagine that you are waiting in your car or a in long line at a mass vaccination center for thirty minutes or longer.

- What's on your mind?
- What are you focusing on?

If your attention is focused internally on your fear, anxiety, and uncomfortable physical sensations such as clenching your jaw or feeling your heart beat rapidly, then all of these psychological and physical experiences will likely make you more nervous. Countering this internal focus requires that you purposefully shift your attention either primarily outward or inward, but with a focus on an imagined calm and tranquility. In short, distraction is not a passive process but an active one (Balanyuk et al., 2018).

WHY DISTRACTION WORKS

. . . .

We know from science that there are five basic reasons (or mechanisms) that explain why distraction works to reduce anxiety, fear, and even pain. Each of these theories is described below. If you know why a technique such as distraction works, then you are more inclined to try it out and benefit from it.

- *Limited Attentional Capacity Theory*
  Your attentional capacity is finite. If you invest in attending to one area of focus, then you have less capacity to focus elsewhere. Note: this also explains why multitasking does

not work with regard to the effectiveness and quality of your focus or attention.

- *Multiple Resources Theory*
  From the moment you are born, your brain is bombarded by an enormous amount of information about yourself (internal stimuli) and the world around you (external stimuli). All of these internal and external stimuli compete for your full attention. It's as if you are doing something and a small child is tugging on your arm demanding your full attention.

- *Neurocognitive Theory*
  Fear, anxiety, and pain rapidly overwhelm your attention. This is a physiologically based, survival-driven reaction. This is normal, natural, and beneficial. Despite this biological drive to fully attend to the source of the threat (e.g., the needle), you can engage your mind to override this rapid reaction by directing your attention away from the threat. This requires energy and effort, but it works for many people and situations.

- *Behavioral Learning Theory*
  Ivan Pavlov, a Russian physiologist, discovered that any object or event could trigger a response. He found that dogs learned to associate objects or things with food (e.g., the food bowl or the assistant who brought them the food) which made them salivate on sight. He coined the term for this behavior "classical conditioning." This theory suggests that we learn to develop a fear of or to associate pain with needles. To "uncouple" the pairing of an object (e.g., seeing a photo of a needle) or event (e.g., scheduling the vaccine), purposeful

distraction may "counter condition" the link between the two. Another way for you to do so is to elicit a response such as relaxation, which is the opposite of fear or anxiety.

- *Neurobiological Theory*

  This theory is a purely biological or neuroscientific explanation of why distraction works. Pain is experienced at the site of the "injury," such as the point of needle insertion, and in the brain. Pain can be controlled in two places: at the site of the "injury" and in specific areas of the brain such as the prefrontal cortex. In essence, when this part of the brain is activated by deliberately engaging in distraction, you quite literally keep pain out of mind. This is why planning to distract yourself works for many.

MENU OF DISTRACTION TECHNIQUES

There are far too many distraction techniques to list here, but this is good news for you. Why? Because you have more options, and you can also mix and match these techniques to find the "right one." Seven distraction techniques are presented below:

- Mindful moist technique
- Imagine a soothing place
- Listen to music
- Use a stress ball
- Watch a film/cartoon
- Virtual reality (VR)
- Applied Tension Technique (ATT)

Table 5 shows the senses that come to life for each of the seven distraction techniques presented in this chapter.

Sense	Distraction Technique
Visual (see)	• Imagine a soothing place • Watch a film/cartoon • Virtual reality (VR)
Auditory (hear)	• Listen to music • Watch a film/cartoon • Virtual reality (VR)
Kinesthetic (touch)	• Mindful moist technique • Use a stress ball • Applied Tension Technique (ATT)
Olfactory (smell)	• Apply essential oil on your write (aromatherapy).
Gustatory (taste)	• Chew flavored gum. • Mindful moist technique (using flavored gum)

Mindful Moist Technique

Like many people, you may experience dry mouth when you are about to get a shot. This is a normal stress response. However, it is still unpleasant. Try chewing gum or squeezing the tip of your tongue. As you do so, you produce saliva (Balanyuk et al., 2018) that moistens your mouth.

Another way to practice the Mindful Moist Technique is to follow these three steps below.

1. Acknowledge that are fearful or anxious as evidenced by dryness in your mouth.

2. Take a sip of water. Hold the water for a moment and then swallow. Notice the sensation of wetness, coolness, and moisture in your mouth.

3. Take a larger sip of water. Hold the water until your tongue becomes completely coated with the refreshing water. Gently swallow the water noticing a sense of calm.

Adapted: St. Richard's Hospice Caring for Life. Reg. Charity No. 515668

Imagine a Soothing Place

Picture a geographic place associated with feelings of calmness, safety, and even confidence. The place can be actual or imagined. Visualize this place while waiting for and during the vaccination. In one study, visualizing calm, tranquil, and safe places offered relief to those with needle phobia during an otherwise incredibly challenging experience (Andrews & Shaw, 2010).

Listen to Music

Take your earbuds or headphones with you as your trusted companion on your way to getting a shot and during the shot. Music listeners find they often "lose themselves" in the sounds. Let the music massage away those fears and anxieties about the needle and vaccine. Studies have shown that music has helped in reducing anxiety and pain (Jayakar & Alter, 2017).

Use a Stress Ball

Pack your stress ball with you as you make your way to the vaccination site and pull it out while waiting for your name to be called. Squeezing and tossing a stress ball back and forth not only diverts your attention but also uses energy. While tossing the stress ball or bobbing it up and down on your leg, you are likely to look at the ball to keep it in play. Interestingly, dialysis patients who used stress balls had less stress than those patients who did not use them (Kasar, Erzincanli, & Akbas, 2020). If you are still not convinced, patients who underwent surgery for varicose veins and used stress balls experienced less anxiety than those not using stress balls (Hudson et al., 2015).

Watch a Film/Cartoon

When you watch a film or cartoon, your attention is pulled into the sounds and visual scenes. Simply averting your visual and cognitive attention to what is happening on the screen lessens your focus on the needle and the vaccination process. You have surely had the experience of being so engrossed in watching something that you did not hear somebody call your name more than once or even walk in front of you quickly. In a randomized controlled trial among patients who underwent minimally invasive surgery in a varicose vein clinic, those who watched a DVD reported less anxiety (Hudson et al., 2015).

In another study, children who watched cartoons experienced less distress than children distracted by more traditional methods used by the nursing team (Cerne et al., 2014). There is no doubt that there is something special about humor. Scientists know that humor is an effective tool for dealing with negative life situations (Labott & Martin, 1987). When you find anything funny, you engage physically when you laugh, and doing so also engages multiple senses.

Virtual Reality

Virtual reality (VR) is increasingly popular as a form of entertainment, a type of training, and even treatment for several psychological disorders, from anxiety to post-traumatic stress disorder (PTSD). A specialized form of VR used to treat those with specific phobias, ranging from fear of snakes to fear of needles, is known as virtual reality exposure therapy (VRET). Remember, chapter 5 walked you through exposure therapy. Again, exposure therapy is the "gold standard" for treating needle phobias.

A single session of VRET is effective in decreasing the fear of injections and changing the way people think about such fear-inducing situations, such as a mass vaccination site (Jiang et al., 2020). VRET has also been shown to be effective in treating dental phobia by reducing dental anxiety (Gujjar et al., 2019).

To benefit from the virtual reality technique, a VR headset is required, such as the one shown below. They range in price, from affordable to expensive. If you reach out to a licensed healthcare practitioner who has been trained in using VRET in particular, they will let you know the best type of VR equipment to buy.

You will note that when you put on the VR headset, you can only see what is projected. Some VR headsets also have earbuds, which direct your attention to specific sounds being played rather than focusing on sounds of the external environment.

Applied Tension Technique (ATT)

In chapter 3, you learned about ATT as a way to reduce the chances of fainting while getting an injection. This technique also distracts you from focusing on the needle by drawing attention to the tensing and relaxing of the major muscle groups. Remember that if you have a history of light-headedness, dizziness, or fainting, then this technique offers an added benefit.

HIGHLIGHTS TO RECALL

In this chapter, you learned about five mechanisms through which distraction works to ease your fears and anxieties around immunization, blood draws, and even dental procedures.

In addition, this chapter offered seven different ways to distract yourself while getting an injection. If one technique does not work, then move to another. Even if you tried a technique several years ago that did not work, this does not mean that it will not work now. Be open and experiment.

Remember that all seven of these distraction techniques are portable.

- Mindful moist technique
- Imagine a soothing place
- Listen to music
- Use a stress ball
- Watch a film/cartoon
- Virtual reality (VR)
- Applied Tension Technique (ATT)

Be sure to take these tools with you during your appointment. The only technique that may be a bit challenging to take with you is a VR headset, but people have done that too. Now, you will focus on another technique that works for many to conquer needle fears and phobias—mindfulness.

Chapter 8 introduces you to mindfulness and shows you how it can be incorporated into your daily life as another go-to technique to relieve yourself of any fear, anxiety, or suffering caused by needles. Be present as you turn the page to the next chapter...being fully aware as you transition from chapter 7 to chapter 8...even noticing your breathing.

TIPS FOR EDUCATORS, HEALTHCARE PROFESSIONALS, AND THERAPISTS

Distraction techniques are not the first-line treatment for specific phobias, including needle phobia (Barlow et al., 2015; Chambless et al., 1998; Steinman et al., 2015). Furthermore, to date, there is no evidence regarding the efficacy of visual distraction in reducing procedural pain or of musical distraction in reducing both procedural pain and fear (Boerner et al., 2015).

Psychoeducation

There is a widespread myth that knowledge does not result in behavioral changes. Yet, psychoeducation is part of cognitive behavioral therapy (CBT) or cognitive behavioral therapy for insomnia (CBT-I) (Kazantzis et al., 2018). Moreover, the psychoeducational component of CBT-I in a meta-analytic review demonstrated small effect sizes (Kazantzis et al., 2018). Granted, psychoeducation may not be the most powerful intervention available to all healthcare practitioners but it's not useless either.

Instructional Plan: Distraction Techniques

An important part of helping the patient enhance their repertoire of tools to use while getting vaccinated is explaining why distraction works. This may increase their perceived relevance of the tool and increase their motivation to use the tool. Five theories explain how and why distraction is efficacious (Birnie et al., 2017).

- Limited Attentional Capacity Theory
- Multiple Resources Theory
- Neurocognitive Theory
- Behavioral Learning Theory
- Neurobiological Theory

After explaining the mechanism of distraction, in part to demonstrate the rationale for this seemingly "common sense" technique, it is best to offer the client or patient an array of options for them to choose from. By offering the client or patient several options, you are moving away from a paternalistic approach to a more autonomous approach. This approach is often referred to as shared decision-making.

Promoting Shared Decision-Making

In this model of care, the healthcare practitioner rightfully remains the expert but also recognizes that the client or patient is the expert of their own experience, values, and preferences. In a *JAMA* article titled "The New Age of Patient Autonomy: Implications for the

Patient-Physician Relationship," Kilbride and Joffe (2018) defined shared decision-making as follows:

> "...shared decision-making involves the physician and patient working together to make medical decisions that accord with the patient's values and preferences. Ideally, the physician and patient engage in an information volley—the physician provides information about the range of options, and the patient expresses his or her values and preferences..."

This focus on autonomy is related to the self-determination theory (SDT), which posits that various emotions exist along a continuum of autonomy (Deci & Ryan, 1985). It is beyond the scope of this book to expand further on SDT, but remember that retaining the autonomy of the client or patient offers many benefits.

REFERENCES

Andrews, G. J., & Shaw, D. (2010). So we started talking about a beach in Barbados: visualization practices and needle phobia. *Social Science and Medicine*, 71(10), 1804-1810.

Balanyuk, I., Ledonne, G., Provenzano, M., Bianco, R., Meroni, C., Ferri, P., & Bonetti, L. (2018). Distraction technique for pain reduction in peripheral venous Catheterization: randomized, controlled trial. *Acta Bio-Medica: Atenei Parmensis*, 89(4-S)(Suppl 4), 55-63.

Birnie, K. A., Chambers, C. T., & Spellman, C. M. (2017). Mechanisms of distraction in acute pain perception and modulation. *Pain*, 158(6), 1012-1013.

Boerner, K. E. et al. (2015). Simple psychological interventions for reducing pain for common needle procedures in adults: systematic review of randomized and quasi-randomized controlled trials. *Clinical Journal of Pain*, 31(10)(Suppl), S90-S98.

Cerne, D., Sannino, L., & Petean, M. (2014). A randomized controlled trial examining the effectiveness of cartoons a distraction technique. *Nursing Children and Young People*, 27(3), 28-33.

Deci, E. L., & Ryan, R. M. (1985). Intrinsic motivation and self-determination in human behavior. New York: Plenum.

Gujjar, K. R., Sharma, R., & Jongh, A. D. (2017). Virtual reality exposure therapy for treatment of dental phobia. *Dental Update*, 44(5), 423-4, 427.

Hudson, B. F., Ogden, J., & Whiteley, M. S. (2015). Randomized controlled trial to compare the effect of simple distraction interventions on pain and anxiety experienced during conscious surgery. *European Journal of Pain*, 19(10), 1447-1455.

Jayakar, J. P., & Alter, D. A. (2017). Music for anxiety reduction in patients undergoing cardiac catheterization: a systematic review and meta-analysis of randomized controlled trials. *Complementary Therapies in Clinical Practice*, 28, 122-130.

Jiang, M. Y. W., Upton, E., & Newby, J. M. (2020). A randomised wait-list controlled pilot trial of one-session virtual reality exposure therapy for blood-injection-injury phobias. *Journal of Affective Disorders*, 276, 636-645.

Kasar, K. S., Erzincanli, S., & Akbas, N. T. (2020). The effect of a stress ball on stress, vital signs and patient comfort in hemodialysis patients: A randomized controlled trial. *Complementary Therapies in Clinical Practice*, 41, 101243.

Kazantzis, N., Luong, H. K., Usatoff, A. S., Impala, T., Yew, R. Y., & Hofmann, S. G. (2018). The processes of cognitive behavioral therapy: a review of meta-analyses. *Cognitive Therapy and Research*, 42(4), 349-357.

Kilbride, M. K., & Joffe, S. (2018). The new age of patient autonomy: implications for the patient–physician relationship. *JAMA*, 320(19), 1973-1974.

Labott, S. M., & Martin, R. B. (1987). The stress-moderating effects of weeping and humor. *Journal of Human Stress*, 13(4), 159-164.

CHAPTER 8

MINDFULNESS

MINDFULNESS OCCURS NATURALLY. It is simply paying attention and noticing what is present in the moment. Mindfulness emphasizes awareness of your body and enables you to notice subtle changes. At the first sign of stress about a vaccine or shot, you can bring mindful awareness to the situation and discover how to dissipate stress rather than exacerbate it.

This chapter offers another tool that can be used to conquer needle fears and phobias, not to mention numerous other forms of anxiety and stress. After reading this chapter, you will understand how mindfulness relates to and also differs from meditation. You will also learn how to tap into a natural state of mindfulness and leverage this tool when you wish to do so. This will help you realize that mindfulness is a skill. Like most skills, you can practice this both formally and informally. Finally, similar to the other tools described in this book, mindfulness is a portable tool. You can take this tool with you wherever you go.

MINDFULNESS AND MEDITATION: SIMILAR BUT DIFFERENT

Is there a difference between mindfulness and meditation? Yes. Meditation is an intentional practice designed to bring about a state of serenity, awareness, or emotional balance by focusing. Meditation has its roots in ancient spiritual and religious traditions. There are many forms of meditation. Most forms of meditation include the following four elements:

- a quiet setting (with as few distractions as possible)
- a specific, comfortable position (sitting, lying down, walking, etc.)
- a focus of attention (a word or set of words, an object, breathing patterns, etc.)
- an open attitude (allowing distractions)

In contrast, mindfulness refers to nonjudgmental awareness of the present moment by simply noticing and accepting our evolving experiences, feelings, thoughts, and physical sensations (Kabat-Zinn, 2003). Mindfulness is a form of meditation. My intention is not to confuse you, but you should know that there is also such a thing as mindfulness meditation.

MINDFULNESS MEDITATION

Mindfulness meditation is a form of meditation. Mindfulness meditation can be guided by you or by others. When guided by others, another person does not have to be present. You can use a

CD or smartphone application. In short, mindfulness meditation can be practiced wherever you are. This makes it another go-to tool to use to conquer your needle fear or phobia. Not only is it portable, but scientific evidence also suggests that it works. In a rigorous scientific study of women undergoing breast biopsy, those assigned to the guided meditation group experienced less anxiety during breast biopsy than those assigned to the focused breathing group and standard care group (Ratcliff et al., 2019).

THREE TYPES OF MINDFULNESS MEDITATION

There are three types of mindfulness meditation: focused attention, or FAM (Lutz et al., 2008); choiceless awareness (Garrison et al., 2015); and loving-kindness meditation, or LKM (Vago & Silbersweig, 2012). Each of these is described below.

FAM

During FAM, you narrowly attend to an object or event. An object can be internal, such as your breathing, or external, such as a painting. An example of an event is listening to sounds as you walk. Select an object that involves a natural scene. Why? Mindfulness is proven to promote psychological well-being, especially when the focus of attention is on landscapes (Dutcher et al., 2021).

Let's practice FAM using an image.

Take a look at the image above with soft eyes and focus on one very small but specific object. It may be one of the sailors, the number 2 on the sail, one of the clouds, or just one of the ripples in the water. Gently maintain your focus. If your eyes and mind wander, that's okay. It is both natural and normal. Simply refocus. Remember that what you fight, you energize. What you energize, you amplify.

Helpful Tip: Find an image that calms and soothes you. It may be a photo from your own album or the internet. The image can be downloaded, printed, and pasted onto a piece of paper or file card. Then, take this calming and soothing image with you. While you wait for your appointment, take it out and focus on it. While you remain seated in the chair, ask them if you can hold this in your hands or have them place it within your frame of vision. Remember that this is not the only solution; it is one of many that you have discovered and will discover as you read this book.

Choiceless Awareness

During choiceless awareness, which is also known as open monitoring meditation (OMM), you attend to awareness itself, not a specific object or event. This is somewhat more challenging. As such, you should try this after you become comfortable with FAM.

LKM

During LKM, you focus on cultivating compassion and love for yourself, and then for others. LKM combines both FAM and OMM. As such, this technique should be attempted after you become comfortable with FAM and OMM.

Mindfulness meditation is similar to mental training programs. The goal is to increase mindful awareness in daily life.

TYPES OF PAIN

The main focus of this book is fear, anxiety, and phobia. The reality is that pain is a real concern during many medical or dental procedures involving an injection. There are two types of pain: physical and psychological. Physical pain is the actual raw sensation of pain in the body, whereas psychological pain refers to the associated stress, anxiety, and frustration.

Physical pain is an actual physiological sensation. Psychological pain involves emotional anticipation and responses to a physical experience. There is a difference between the sensation of physical pain and all the other meanings you assign to pain. Be careful not to catastrophize the physical sensation of pain.

Do I catastrophize my pain?

Catastrophizing happens when you experience a lack of confidence and control. Consequently, you amplify your expectations of negative outcomes (Sullivan & D'Eon, 1990). You may feel fine while the phlebotomist rubs alcohol on the skin of your arm, and then, in an instant, you may experience full-blown terror. This may cause you to escape from these intense negative feelings or avoid other situations involving needles. Researchers have found that pain catastrophizing is connected to pain-related fear avoidance (Crombez et al., 2012). Mindfulness meditation, particularly when focusing on an external object as a distraction, has been found to reduce pain catastrophizing (Dorado et al., 2018).

MINDFULNESS AND PAIN

Through mindfulness, you can begin to let go of psychological pain so that only physical pain remains. When psychological pain begins to diminish, muscle tension around the area of physical pain begins to reduce, and this mitigates perceptions of pain.

For some, focusing on the needle offers relief from fear, anxiety, and pain. Therefore, if your shoulder feels the prick of the needle, instead of distracting yourself or reacting in some other way, you should try to focus on the area of physical pain with mindful awareness. This involves perceiving the pain area with an attitude of curiosity, compassion, kindness, and acknowledgment. This will not be easy at first, but you will get better with practice.

A word of caution is necessary here. Some people find that bringing their mindful awareness to the present moment while being injected increases pain and distress. If this is the case for you, do not do it. If this is your experience, then attend to an external object as the focus of your attention, using the FAM that has been discussed in an earlier section in this chapter.

HOW MINDFULNESS WORKS

You may believe that mindfulness is simply doing nothing. It may even look as though a person who is engaged in the formal practice of mindfulness is wasting their time by just standing or sitting in one spot. This is false.

Mindful breathing activates the parasympathetic nervous system, which is your body's "rest and digest" system. The sympathetic system is your body's "fight, flight, or freeze" response. To dial down your "fight, flight, or freeze" system, you must activate your "rest and digest" system by using any of the following tools presented in this book:

- self-hypnosis
- positive self-talk
- Applied Tension Technique (ATT)
- mindfulness meditation

When the parasympathetic nervous system, or "rest and digest" system, is activated, heart rate and blood pressure decrease, which can help reduce anxiety and stress. Mindfulness meditation lowers reactivity to threats (Brown & Ryan, 2003).

MINDFUL TOOLS TO USE WHILE GETTING A SHOT

The first part of this chapter focuses on getting you ready for your vaccination. You may wonder which tools will be available to you right before you get the shot or even while you are being injected.

Sensory Check-In

Do a quick sensory check-in by naming one thing you are experiencing through each of your senses. Look around and name one thing you see. Take a deep breath and name one thing you smell. Close your eyes and name one thing you hear. Run your tongue around your teeth, swallow, and name the taste in the mouth. Reach your hand out, touch something, and name the texture that you feel.

Mindfulness as a Prevention Technique

Mindfulness can be used as an on-the-spot technique after you feel the rush of hormones flowing through your body, the flood of thoughts racing through your mind, and the disturbing physical sensations. In short, if you are on a high cliff of anxiety, fear, and distress, then purposefully engaging in a mindfulness meditation technique will help you descend from the high cliff over time. The image below depicts how engaging in mindfulness as a formal and informal practice can enable you to move from a state of high anxiety to less anxiety and fear. Are you ready to get off the cliff of high anxiety?

Mindfulness is even more powerful as a *prevention* tool in decreasing reactivity to situations such as immunization. Imagine that you are on your smartphone, searching for places where you can get a vaccine: with each swipe of the phone, the sweat on your fingertips makes it more difficult to swipe. You realize you are holding your breath. You are swaying back and forth in a jagged rhythm. What do you do?

First, notice what is happening right here and now in this present moment. *Second*, practice one of your mindfulness meditation tools. For example, you can focus on an external object—your breath or something around you. Alternatively, you can find a relaxing image on your phone or listen to a musical piece that calms and grounds you. *Third*, give yourself some time to stop climbing the cliff of high anxiety, fear, and phobia. *Fourth*, as you feel your "rest and digest" system kicking into gear, focus on positive feelings, comforting thoughts, and pleasant physical sensations, irrespective of how small, tiny, or insignificant they may seem.

> Mindfulness meditation is a tool for all seasons,
> not just the seasons of stress and distress.

DESIGNING YOUR MINDFULNESS PRACTICE SCHEDULE: MINDFULNESS IN 5 MINUTES OR LESS

You may say, "I don't have time for this stuff!" Did you know that there are 1,440 minutes in a day? Did you also know that research has shown that practicing mindfulness meditation for 5 minutes a day yields beneficial outcomes? (Howarth et al., 2019). I am sure that you can spare 5 minutes out of the 1,440 minutes in your day. Do not say you do not have time! Be honest and say that it is not a priority now. That is okay.

There are many ways to cultivate mindfulness. One way is to breathe mindfully. To breathe mindfully is to focus your attention on your own breathing. You will enjoy many benefits ranging from reduced anxiety to improved ability to focus and concentrate.

Breathing Mindfully Meditation in Under 5 Minutes or Less

Try the breathing mindfully meditation by following these 4 simple directions.

1. *Find a comfortable posture.*
   You can do this while standing, but ideally you should be sitting or lying down in a comfortable position. Your eyes may be open or closed, but you may find it easier to maintain your focus if you close your eyes.

2. *Become aware of the sensations of breathing.*

Draw your attention to your breathing, just as it is here and now. You do not need to make your breathing any different than it naturally is. You do not have to make it slower or deeper. Just draw your attention to your natural breathing, with an attitude of curiosity and kindness. Notice the movement of air as you breathe in, inhaling oxygen, and as you breathe out, exhaling carbon dioxide. As you breathe in and out, tell yourself in a gentle voice, "Breathing in, I know that I am breathing in" and "Breathing out, I know that I am breathing out." Alternatively, you can shorten this to "In . . . Out . . ."

Breathe normally and try to become a focused observer of your breathing. It is helpful to focus on one physical cue, such as the rise and fall of your chest or the sensation of air in your nostrils (cool air coming in, warm air going out).

3. *Continue to meditate without trying to control the depth or speed of your breathing.*

When your mind wanders (and it inevitably will), make a note of it, then simply refocus on each act of inhalation and exhalation. Allow your thoughts to drift past you.

4. *After 10 minutes, gently open your eyes.*

As you open your eyes, softly open up your senses too. Widen your awareness of your act of breathing in and out. Wear a warm smile on your face to dissolve any self-evaluation, self-judgment, and self-criticism about how effective your mindful breathing was. Breathing is natural, automatic, and effortless. All you did was slow down to notice what you do every waking second of your life.

Like any tool, you will get better with practice. You may also benefit from mindfulness applications.

MINDFULNESS APPLICATIONS 101

There are hundreds, if not thousands, of mindfulness and meditation applications in the application store. A meta-analytic study (a study involving analysis of the findings of multiple studies) found that mindfulness results in these benefits (Gál et al., 2021):

- less perceived stress
- fewer symptoms of depression and anxiety
- higher life satisfaction
- higher quality of life
- less burnout
- better psychological well-being
- greater positive affect
- less negative affect

This list is not exhaustive. The key is to fully complete the meditation sessions facilitated by the application. Why? The same study found that, on average, 43 percent of mindfulness meditation sessions had been completed.

HIGHLIGHTS TO RECALL

Mindfulness is a topic that you read about, hear about, and see all over the media. The goal of this chapter is to expose you to the basics of mindfulness and mindfulness meditation in order to help you conquer your fear or phobia related to needles of any kind. Reading this chapter will not make you a master of mindfulness, but hopefully you will be able to:

- Orient yourself to this natural and normal state of mindful awareness.
- Recognize early signs of distress and apply a mindfulness meditation technique.
- Turn off the "fight, flight, or freeze" response by using one of your mindfulness meditation tools to get you off that high cliff of anxiety and fear.
- Purposefully practice mindfulness to decrease reactivity to events and situations of all types, particularly those involving injections and needles.
- Be honest with yourself about having at least five minutes to practice but also be real with yourself, realize that this may not be important to you at this time in your life, and accept that that's okay.

The next technique you will learn is assertiveness, though some of you may already be masters of assertiveness. Chapter 9 will focus on assertiveness. In this chapter, you will learn the difference between assertiveness and aggressiveness. You will also learn the difference between assertiveness and accommodation (being a doormat). Assertiveness involves claiming your voice and expressing your thoughts and feelings to ensure that you are noticed, heard, seen, acknowledged, and respected. Turn to chapter 9—it's time to speak up for yourself and advocate for what you need and deserve.

TIPS FOR EDUCATORS, HEALTHCARE PROFESSIONALS, AND THERAPISTS

Mindfulness is not the first-line treatment for specific phobias such as needle phobia. However, the literature suggests that mindfulness is clinically efficacious in reducing both anxiety and depression (Rodrigues et al., 2017). In a randomized controlled trial, mindfulness applications (e.g., Pacific) were found to be clinically efficacious in reducing anxiety (Moberg et al., 2019).

Recommending applications (apps) is beyond the scope of this book. However, health applications are widely used. The number of users will soon exceed two hundred fifty thousand (Hsin & Torous, 2018), and there are more than three hundred apps in the US iOS App store alone (Powell et al., 2019). In this regard, a few observations are necessary. As a healthcare practitioner, you must be careful about prescribing applications. In the United States, there is no liability protection for doing so. In contrast, in the United Kingdom, the National Health Service (2018) places the burden of demonstrating safety and efficacy on the application developer rather than on the prescriber. The good news is that the Food and Drug Administration has launched the Digital Center of Health Excellence, which is establishing guidelines for the emerging field of digital therapeutics.

Mindfulness is a specific technique that is supported by growing evidence. As such, you should be trained in the use of this technique and know when it is clinically indicated. Before guiding your clients or patients through mindfulness or even before recommending mindfulness, it may be prudent to receive mindfulness training (e.g., a one- or two-day course). Indeed, at present, there are graduate programs in mindfulness and certificate programs that span several days.

REFERENCES

Brown, K.W., & Ryan, R.M. (2003). The benefits of being present: mindfulness and its role in psychological well-being. *Journal of Personality and Social Psychology*, 84(4), 822-848.

Crombez, G., Eccleston, C., Van Damme, S., Vlaeyen, J.W., & Karoly, P. (2012). Fear-avoidance model of chronic pain: the next generation. *Clinical Journal of Pain*, 28(6), 475-483.

Dorado, K., Schreiber, K.L., Koulouris, A., Edwards, R.R., Napadow, V., & Lazaridou, A. (2018). Interactive effects of pain catastrophizing and mindfulness on pain intensity in women with fibromyalgia. *Health Psychology Open*, 5(2), 2055102918807406.

Dutcher, J.M., Boyle, C.C., Eisenberger, N.I., Cole, S.W., & Bower, J.E. (2021). Neural responses to threat and reward and changes in inflammation following a mindfulness intervention. *Psychoneuroendocrinology*, 125, 105114.

Gál, É., Ştefan, S., & Cristea, I.A. (2021). The efficacy of mindfulness meditation apps in enhancing users' well-being and mental health related outcomes: a meta-analysis of randomized controlled trials. *Journal of Affective Disorders*, 279, 131-142.

Garrison, K.A., Zeffiro, T.A., Scheinost, D., Constable, R.T., & Brewer, J.A. (2015). Meditation leads to reduced default mode network activity beyond an active task. *Cognitive, Affective and Behavioral Neuroscience*, 15(3), 712-720.

Howarth, A., Smith, J.G., Perkins-Porras, L., & Ussher, M. (2019). Effects of brief mindfulness-based interventions on health-related outcomes: a systematic review. *Mindfulness*, 10(10), 1957-1968.

Hsin, H., & Torous, J. (2018). Creating boundaries to empower digital health technology. *British Journal of Psychology Open*, 4(4), 235-237.

Kabat-Zinn, J. (2003). Mindfulness-based interventions in context: past, present, and future. *Clinical Psychology: Science and Practice*, 10(2), 144-156.

Lutz, A., Slagter, H.A., Dunne, J.D., & Davidson, R.J. (2008). Attention regulation and monitoring in meditation. *Trends in Cognitive Sciences*, 12(4), 163-169.

Moberg, C., Niles, A., & Beermann, D. (2019). Guided self-help works randomized waitlist controlled trial of Pacifica, a mobile app integrating cognitive behavioral therapy and mindfulness for stress, anxiety, and depression. *Journal of Medical Internet Research*, 21(6), e12556.

NHS. Disclaimer. NHS, 2018 (https://www.nhs.uk/apps-library/disclaimer/).

Powell, A.C., Yue, Z., Shan, C., & Torous, J.B. (2019). The monetization strategies of apps for anxiety management: an international comparison. *Journal of Technology in Behavioral Science*, 4(2), 67-72. https://doi.org/10.1007/s41347-019-00093-y.

Ratcliff, C.G., Prinsloo, S., Chaoul, A., Zepeda, S.G., Cannon, R., Spelman, A., ... & Cohen, L. (2019). A randomized controlled trial of brief mindfulness meditation for women undergoing stereotactic breast biopsy. *Journal of the American College of Radiology: JACR*, 16(5), 691-699.

Rodrigues, M.F., Nardi, A.E., & Levitan, M. (2017). Mindfulness in mood and anxiety disorders: a review of the literature. *Trends in Psychiatry and Psychotherapy*, 39(3), 207-215.

Sullivan, M.J., & D'Eon, J.L. (1990). Relation between catastrophizing and depression in chronic pain patients. *Journal of Abnormal Psychology*, 99(3), 260-263.

Vago, D.R., & Silbersweig, D.A. (2012). Self-awareness, self-regulation, and self-transcendence (S-ART): a framework for understanding the neurobiological mechanisms of mindfulness. *Frontiers in Human Neuroscience*, 6, 296. https://doi.org/10.3389/fnhum.2012.00296

RESOURCES

UCLA's Mindfulness Awareness Research Center (https://www.uclahealth.org/marc/).

CHAPTER 9

ASSERTIVENESS

ASSERTIVENESS WAS A "hot topic" in the 1970s and the 1980s, coming out of the Civil Rights Revolution. Since the 1980s, assertiveness has fallen into the background. However, it is no less important today than it was in the past. The #MeToo, BLM, and Say Her Name movements are expressions of assertiveness. The focus of chapter 9 is assertiveness as a behavioral style and as a set of techniques to express your needs clearly and confidently when in the presence of a healthcare provider in any setting. Our specific focus in this book is dental or medical situations involving a needle, injection, or blood draw.

After reading chapter 9 on assertiveness, you will be much closer to interacting with healthcare providers by:

- carrying yourself in such a way that others know you value your ability to choose what is best for you
- signaling that you are in your charge of your body

- demonstrating that you are the expert in your own thoughts, feelings, and sensations of your own body
- articulating, without being obnoxious, that you are knowledgeable (if you have done your homework)
- informing them of your preferences and choices
- standing up for yourself if you feel violated or ignored in any way

The six assertiveness topics presented in this chapter lay the foundation for additional tools to be added to your growing toolkit to conquer your needle fear or phobia. We begin this chapter by first highlighting the differences among assertiveness, aggressiveness, passiveness, and passive-aggressiveness. Experts in communication call these the four behavioral styles.

THE FOUR BEHAVIORAL STYLES: HOW ARE YOU PERCEIVED?

There are four behavioral styles and each one will be described below with an example of how this style may appear in a setting involving needles.

Assertive: When you are assertive, you express your wants, feelings, needs, and choices. Underlying this style is the fact that you believe in your own autonomy and agency. In other words, you and your voice matter. When you are assertive, it does not mean that you shut others down. This means that there are at least two voices in the room.

> **Sarah** is sitting in the dental chair getting ready to get a shot of pain killer before taking out her wisdom tooth. Sarah turns around facing the dental hygienist and confidently says, "Excuse me. I prefer that you deaden the surface with the cold spray before inserting the needle. Thank you."

Aggressive: When you are aggressive, you express your demands and dictate by forcing your will on the other person. Your voice is the loudest. Your voice is also, at times, the only voice in the room. For the other person, they may feel attacked, ignored, or threatened. This may trigger the "fight, flight, or freeze" response. If they are triggered, it makes no sense to keep communicating because they cannot listen. A word of caution here: when some people are confronted with aggressiveness by you or others, some will want to "pay you back."

> **Roger** is standing in line at the mass vaccination center and the vaccinator asks Roger to roll up his right sleeve. Rogers says, "Put the needle on the left, not the right" as he unrolls his left sleeve and turns his body around to get the vaccine in the left arm. He then says, "You better not hurt me either. I don't like &^$%^ needles. You got it?"

Passive: When you are passive, you withhold from voicing your wants, feelings, needs, and choices. You decide not to share them. You may expect the other person to "read your mind." You may expect the other person to "really know you if they care about or love you." Over time, you may feel as if your voice does not matter and that, to some, you do not matter.

Fatema is waiting for her blood to be drawn for the lab tests ordered by her primary care physician. She knows that there is one specific spot on her right arm where phlebotomists do not have any problems with getting her blood. She is fearful that the phlebotomist will stick her multiple times unnecessarily. Fatema goes back and forth in her head about whether she should say something or not. She thinks to herself that the phlebotomist most likely knows about these two specific spots anyway. Fatema is silent, not silenced. She is stuck not once, not twice, but three times.

Passive-Aggressive: When you are passive aggressive, you subtly, indirectly, and somewhat secretly express your wants, feelings, needs, and choices. You may say one thing, but your body language, including your facial expressions, says something else. When you are passive-aggressive, you may not express what is important to you to the other person, but instead express it to others voiced as a complaint, not the expression of your wants, feelings, needs, and choices.

Manuel enters the dermatology office for a biopsy (removal of tissue) on the side of his face near his left nostril, where there is a black bump. The nurse cleans and sanitizes the surface of the skin. The dermatologist enters the room in about five minutes and then with a sharp instrument takes a piece of the tissue ready to be prepped to go to the lab.

When Manuel saw that sharp biopsy instrument coming toward his face, he "freaked out" internally but said nothing. In fact, the nurse asked Manuel, "Are you feeling worried or concerned about the biopsy procedure today?" He replied, "Okay." He was "freaking out" about the lidocaine needle and the biopsy needle. He wanted the nurse or the dermatologist to apply a topical anesthetic before the lidocaine needle but said nothing.

Manuel was disappointed, more fearful after this experience, and "pissed off." He told his wife about the poor care and then decided to call the Patient Relations Representative to file a complaint against the nurse and the doctor.

WHAT'S MY BEHAVIORAL STYLE?
A RAPID MINI-ASSESSMENT

After reading these descriptions and vignettes, you probably have a good sense of which one of these four behavioral styles is your dominant style and to what degree you can tap into each style depending on the situation and who the other person happens to be.

- Assertive
- Aggressive
- Passive
- Passive-Aggressive

You may show one style with your family and the other with your neighbor. You may be assertive (hopefully not aggressive) with coworkers but passive (hopefully not passive-aggressive) with your boss.

Below are ten questions. Answer each question using this scale:

> **3** = very much like me
>
> **2** = rather like me
>
> **1** = slightly like me
>
> **-1** = slightly unlike me
>
> **-2** = rather unlike me
>
> **-3** = very much unlike me

1. I am quick to express my opinion.
2. I enjoy starting conversations with others, including strangers.
3. I never have a hard time saying "No."
4. I never bottle up my emotions.
5. If somebody asks me to do something, I often ask why.
6. I prefer telling people my concerns to their face rather than sending an email or text.
7. If another person hurts me in some way, I let them know about it.
8. If I buy something I don't like, I return it.
9. If I don't know, I ask.
10. You don't have to guess how I'm feeling or what I'm thinking.

SCORING

Add the total number of points. Your score could range from as **high as 30** to as **low as -30**. The higher the score, the more assertive you are. Remember that you always have to validate any self-assessment based on your own experience. Scores of **20 and above** strongly suggest that your assertiveness is your dominant style or that you can be assertive when you need to. Scores of **-20 and below** strongly suggest that assertiveness is a skill that you should further develop. Assertiveness is not a gene. Assertiveness is a set of skills and a mindset. Mindsets change.

MINDFULNESS MATTERS: FOUNDATION OF ASSERTIVENESS

Chapter 8 focused on being present in the here and now, without judgment, and discussed mindfulness. Mindfulness matters with regard to becoming more assertive. How? The more mindful you are of your thoughts, feelings, and physical sensations, the easier it is to consider voicing your experience to others. If you do not have a clue about what is going on with you, then it is difficult to say anything to somebody else. Whatever thoughts, feelings, and physical sensations arise when you are confronted with needles, try to resist labeling them and judging your thoughts, feelings, and sensations. Notice them instead. Find words to describe them. Voice them to yourself again without labeling or self-judgment. Then, voice them to others in a way that you can be heard, understood, and counted. This is an assertive behavioral style.

COUNT YOUR VOICE FIRST—THE DOOR TO OTHERS COUNTING YOUR VOICE

Does your voice count? Do your thoughts, feelings, and physical sensations matter? Should you let dentists, vaccinators, and phlebotomists know that you are feeling anxious about the needle? YES. When you articulate your voice, you are saying to the other person, "I respect myself. I hold myself in high regard. My thoughts, feelings, and physical sensations are important."

You cannot control the responses of the other person, but you can control the decision to stay silent or to voice what is happening with you and your preferences. Your preferences matter. You matter. A natural question is: "What do I actually say?"

Before getting into some suggested language, consider these three strategies to establish your assertive mindset and send a signal to the other person that your voice matters because you matter.

- Be clear about your expectations and preferences. What do you want? What do you expect the healthcare provider to do and even not to do?
- View your healthcare providers as part of your team. How can you help them offer you the best, least stressful, and satisfying care?
- Resolve problems in a diplomatic way before they escalate.

SCRIPTING: DON'T LEAVE ASSERTIVE COMMUNICATION TO CHANCE

Actors and actresses rehearse, the script writer creates the drama, the producer brings together the resources to make it happen, and the director brings the written word to life on stage or on film. You can see that there are many players involved. Each player has a unique skill set and plays a unique role. The same is true for when you are preparing to get vaccinated, visit the dentist, or get a procedure in which a needle is involved. If you prepare a script for what to say, how to say it, and when to say it, then the experience is likely to be more certain and less stressful. Greater certainty and less stress typically result in greater control.

First, we wanted to combine empathy and assertiveness. You want to try to view the world from the perspective of healthcare practitioners. If you are in line in a mass vaccination center and there around twenty-five people in line, then it is reasonable to expect the vaccinator to feel a bit rushed because of the crowd. As such, you still want to be assertive, but you have to do so in a way that respects the time of the healthcare provider. **Use empathic assertion**.

Second, many people may not hear you the first time. They may be distracted by doing something or be distracted internally. For example, you are in the dental office, and the dentist is masked and gloved up and wearing a face shield. The background has the sounds of drills, voices, and the running of all the machines in a dental office. You say very softly that you are afraid of needles and wish that the dentist would be gentle and inform you of what is happening throughout the procedure. The dentist does not hear you. You have not been silenced. You have not been ignored. You have not been misunderstood. You have simply not been heard because you spoke too softly for the environment. **Speak up and be heard**.

Third, prepare your words with care and deliberation. While using **empathic assertion** and **speak up and be heard**, it is critical that you articulate certain words and phrases below as examples.

- Use "I" Statements. Express your wants and preferences from your perspective. For instance: "I want," "I feel," "I prefer," or "I need."
- Use polite and civil expressions to articulate your feelings, needs, wants, and preferences, in a way that signals respect for the other person and their role. For instance, "Please," "Thank you," and "You made a positive difference in my experience."

Take a look at the My Assertiveness Script Template. You will note that the first two sentences focus on the other person. This is the **empathy** of **empathic assertions**. After interacting with the healthcare provider, you transition to what you need, want, or prefer. This part is about you and your voice. This is where you use the "I" statements, in a confident tone and loud enough for the healthcare provider to hear. After articulating your voice, you end with an expression of politeness and civility. This promotes the relationship between the two of you, humanizes you, and personalizes you.

MY ASSERTIVENESS SCRIPT TEMPLATE

I hope you are having a good day. Has it been busy for you today? Before we begin, I want to let you know that I am afraid of needles. I prefer that you _____. Thank you for your consideration.

WORDS MATTER AND BODY LANGUAGE DOES TOO!

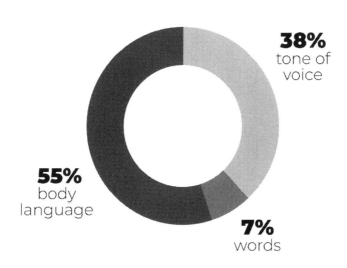

38%
tone of voice

55%
body language

7%
words

Look at this pie chart. What do you notice? You see that when communicating with somebody, words matter, but not as much as we think. Linguists and communication experts found that humans draw meaning from conversations by focusing on nonverbals first, tone of voice second, and the actual words third. Your grandmother probably said it best, "It's not what you say but how you say it." This cliché is true but does not count nonverbals—body language and facial expressions.

Below are two tips on how to engage in **empathic assertion** by using your whole self.

- **Empowered verbal and body language:** Project confidence with an erect posture and direct eye contact. Express yourself with a strong, clear tone and by articulating every word in a fluid, nonstaggered way.
- **Switch your focus if you experience a distressing look or response:** If the response you get from the healthcare provider is either verbally or nonverbally not supportive, or even threatening to you, then switch your focus away from them. Do not dwell on their looks. Lean in if it is good and working, lean away if it is not.

HIGHLIGHTS TO RECALL

Assertiveness is not rude, uncivil, or commanding. Assertiveness is not being a "doormat" or a "pushover." Assertiveness is being seen, heard, and understood. When interacting with others, including healthcare professionals, they know that your voice counts, that your choices and preferences matter. This does not mean that some things may not have to be negotiated and that you will get what you desire

100 percent of the time. This means you will not remain silent and you will not be silenced.

Even before you picked up *Conquer Needle Phobia*, you probably heard about and used the "I" statement technique. Continue to use this technique, but also consider what your style is. Remember that there are four behavioral styles.

- Assertive
- Aggressive
- Passive
- Passive-Aggressive

Your behavioral style matters in order to truly be seen, heard, and understood. The best style is assertive. It opens up doors. Other styles can close doors. Your behavioral style is not determined by your genes or family background. You can change your style by modifying intent and behavior.

As you prepare for your next appointment where you know there will be a needle, try scripting what you will say. You may even want to imagine that you are actually saying it to another person. Visualization is a powerful tool.

Chapter 10, our final chapter, will focus on bringing others with you to appointments if you find that it helps you lessen your fears and anxieties or actually go to the appointment. If you take a family member or friend, encourage them to read chapter 9 so that they can be assertive too and not the other three behavioral styles. Pat yourself on the back for getting to the final chapter of this book and knowing that you now have more tools than when you started. Chapter 10 is waiting for you, so go on and read the first page.

TIPS FOR EDUCATORS, HEALTHCARE PROFESSIONALS, AND THERAPISTS

Assertiveness training is not new. In fact, dating back to the 1950s, Wolpe (1958) described assertiveness training as a core element of psychotherapy. Before the Rathus Assertiveness Scale, practitioners would assess assertiveness based largely on clinical interviews. The Rathus Assertiveness Scale (1973) is a thirty-item self-report scale that provides practitioners with a more reliable and valid way to assess assertiveness.

After assessing the degree of assertiveness the client or patient possesses and their willingness to tap into their own assertiveness in different situations with different people, such as phlebotomists or dentists, utilize an appreciative inquiry (Cooperider et al., 2003), and then ask the following questions:

- Tell me about a time when you felt proud for not just finding your voice but for clearly and confidently expressing your voice. This could be a situation.
- Describe for me a time when you were assertive in getting your wants, preferences, or needs met in a medical or dental situation.

The Appreciative Inquiry (AI) technique draws upon positive psychology. Positive psychology seeks to increase the frequency and intensity of positive emotional experiences through deliberate actions (Huffman et al., 2016). Positive psychology works in various ways. Boiler et al. (2013) showed that positive psychology programs were associated with the following benefits: greater happiness, less depression, and improved overall well-being. In another study using the AI technique, it was found that participants had increased feelings toward their ideal self. This finding is important for clients or patients with a fear of needles because finding and expressing their voice may not always fit with their past or present self, but you want to move them to their ideal self.

Working with clients or patients where the clinical focus is on increasing their assertiveness skills lends itself well to using role-playing after the assessment phase. Moreno (1946) created psychodrama as a type of experiential psychotherapy well suited for working with clients or patients with personal and interpersonal challenges. The key in role-playing is to have the client or patients to talk *to you* rather than *about others* in their relationships, with you playing the part of the "other." In short, it is a live simulation, rather than a virtual reality simulation. Erbay, Reyhani, Ünal, Özcan, Özgöçer, Uçar, & Yıldız (2018) found a reduction in cortisol levels and stress as measured by the Perceived Stress Scale and the State-Trait Anxiety Inventory after a sixteen-week group psychodrama intervention. The key to remember is not this particular style of role-playing, but actually having the client or patient practice with you by saying the words out loud and matching their body language and vocal tone. Deliberate practice increases skills, enhances confidence, and drives competence.

REFERENCES

Bolier, L., Haverman, M., Westerhof, G. J., Riper, H., Smit, F., & Bohlmeijer, E. (2013). Positive psychology interventions: A meta-analysis of randomized controlled studies. *BMC Public Health,* 13(1), 119.

Erbay, L. G., Reyhani, İ., Ünal, S., Özcan, C., Özgöçer, T., Uçar, C., & Yıldız, S. (2018). Does psychodrama affect perceived stress, anxiety-depression scores, and saliva cortisol in patients with depression? *Psychiatry Investigation*, 15(10), 970.

Huffman, J. C., Millstein, R. A., Mastromauro, C. A., Moore, S. V., Celano, C. M., Bedoya, C. A., ... Januzzi, J. L. (2016). A positive psychology intervention for patients with an acute coronary syndrome: Treatment development and proof-of-concept trial. *Journal of Happiness Studies*, 17(5), 1985-2006.

Moreno, J. L. (1946). Psychodrama – First volume. Beacon, NY: Beacon House.

Olayinka, O. D., Moore, S. M., & Stange, K. C. (2020). Pilot test of an appreciative Inquiry intervention in hypertension self-management. *Western Journal of Nursing Research*, 42(7), 543-553.

Rathus, S. A. (1973). A 30-item schedule for assessing assertive behavior. *Behavior Therapy*, 4, 398-406.

Wolpe, J. (1958). Psychotherapy by reciprocal inhibition. Stanford, CA: Stanford University Press.

CHAPTER 10

SOCIAL SUPPORT: FAMILY, FRIENDS, AND OTHERS

GETTING A SHOT or blood drawn—unless you are a child or have a special need—is typically something that you see people do by themselves. It does not have to be this way. There is no rule in the "Big Rule Book" that says, "Thou shall get a needle by yourself." This chapter walks you through the four types of social support: instrumental, emotional, informational, and interpersonal.

After understanding the differences among these types of social support, you will be in a better position to approach a family member, friend, colleague, or another person to give you the kind of support that you need when you need it. The key is knowing how to invite others to provide you with the type of support that you require in order to conquer your fear or phobia of needles. In some cases, you do not even have to ask but simply have to recognize that an offer has been made, and then you have to decide if you would like to accept the offer and how to accept it. Remember, it is okay whether or not you get vaccinated on your own or go with someone else. Bill Withers, the legendary singer, sang lyrics in his hit song "Lean on Me" focusing on strength, friendship, and carrying on by leaning on supportive others.

Before we move to the four types of social support, I would like to share a story about my son Armand, when he was seven or eight years old. He had a dental visit that required a needle before the procedure could be performed. Fearing what I had experienced as a child about the same age, I pledged to myself that I would not let history repeat itself. I'd felt terribly alone, judged, embarrassed, frightened, and in intense pain during my first dental injection and procedure. This experience was like a worn marble step from where the mark would never go away, although it is not as visible and visceral as it was in the past. What did I do?

I first promised myself that I would be supportive—which I will focus on later. Second, I decided to take his best friend, Conrad, with us. I knew that this would work as I had seen Conrad support my son during tough times and Conrad was playful and slightly mischievous. In short, Conrad was a source of distraction and also support. I asked the dentist. She agreed. Then the three of us jumped into the car to head to the dentist's office. Like most dentists' offices, the place was quiet, except for the sound of "dental music," whispering patients and staff, and the occasional sound of a drill or some other mechanical instrument. The dental assistant quietly asked, "Armand, are you ready?" Conrad was the first to respond with a loud, "YES, let us go. We are coming." Armand and I followed Conrad, who was following the dental assistant to the room that had the usual dental equipment, with a few sprinklings of kid-friendly images and a cartoon playing on the television.

Conrad sat in the dental chair, looked at the dentist, and said, "I am ready Dr. Dentist." She smiled and made space for Armand and Conrad to switch places. They did so, although Armand's movement was slightly slower than Conrad's. The dentist explained what was going to happen to Armand. Conrad was fiddling with some instruments on the side and Armand was smiling and laughing quietly. I knew that I had made the right choice to bring Conrad to the visit as this experience was filled with support and humor, and, for me, it was an opportunity to send "good vibes of love" to my son during what could have been the beginning of needle fear, phobia, and dental anxiety. Armand is now twenty-one and he does not even blink an eye when he sees a needle or has to visit the dentist. Social support works (at least for some).

FOUR TYPES OF SOCIAL SUPPORT

There are four types of social support:

- Instrumental
- Emotional
- Informational
- Interpersonal

Instrumental Support

This type of support is practical. You are relieved of having to do something that you do not know how to do or may not have the time to do because your plate is full. Examples may include someone driving you to the mass vaccination center and waiting for you because they know you have a history of fainting when exposed to needles or someone watching your kids while you go to the dentist.

Emotional Support

This is the first type of support that I think of for many people. This type of support focuses on ensuring that you are settled and grounded in how you feel. Examples may include a person listening to you without judging you, showing empathy toward you and your situation, and giving you the space to vent and express whatever you feel and however you feel.

Informational Support

This type of support is based on the provision of helpful hints, tips, tools, and techniques, and it is knowledge based. Examples include sending you a link or video about mindful meditation or sharing information about a new way to relieve needle phobia.

Interpersonal Support

This type of support includes the presence of another person to whom you are connected in some way. For many, interpersonal support is quiet and works just because the other person is present. The photo below shows how natural it is to just be there.

Other examples of "being present" include somebody sitting quietly in the room with you as you get your blood drawn or knowing that somebody is waiting for you when you leave the biopsy procedure room who will welcome you with a warm and embracing smile.

What type of social support did Conrad show toward Armand?

Check off which types are applicable based on the story.

☐ Instrumental
☐ Emotional
☐ Informational
☐ Interpersonal

In the story about Armand and Conrad, it was clear that Conrad was emotionally and interpersonally supportive, not to mention that he acted as an external distraction (in a good way). For me, I tried to be there for Armand with all four types of social support, but I also invited Conrad into our circle of social support. Why? Largely because I knew that Conrad had a special relationship with my son and that only he could engender certain good feelings. Knowing this, I stepped back and allowed Conrad to "work his magic." This story and these four types of social support may nudge you to really reflect on, not just read, these two questions:

- Can you step back and allow others to be supportive of those you love and care about or do you pressure yourself to "be all things to all people"?
- In the future, will you step back and allow others to be supportive of those you love and care about or do you pressure yourself to "be all things to all people"?

SOCIAL SUPPORT: IT IS EASIER THAN YOU THINK

Giving and receiving social support is easier than you think, even though you may have to look beyond your social network. Social psychologists tell us that the number of contacts, friends, likes, or other quantitative metrics have little effect on the quality of our connections. It is the quality that matters, not the quantity, in times of need.

Some of my clients have hundreds—and some even have thousands—of social media connections, yet they feel as if they have no one to turn to during their time of need. Nobody. Other clients may only have three or four connections, but they are strong, dependable, reliable, and nonjudgmental. It is obvious that you can have both, but if you had a choice, what would you choose—quantity or quality?

The Beatles sang a smashing hit song, called "With A Little Help From My Friends," that clearly describes the power of real social support, not simply a social network. In this song, the central message is that with a little help from your friends that you can get by and even try referencing those challenges in life which seem insurmountable.

As this relates to inviting a supportive person in your life, it is important to remember that the person does not have to be a friend but can just be friendly and supportive in a way that counts for you.

BE A GIVER NOT JUST A TAKER: LAW OF RECIPROCITY

It is not all about you. At least, it should not be all about you. When asking for support from others or accepting support from others, be genuinely grateful and demonstrate your appreciation. Do not assume that they know what you feel in your heart. They may, or they may not.

There are six keys to being there for others and also increasing the chances that they will be there for you during your times of need or want.

- *Stay connected.*
  Relationships require continual nourishment, otherwise they go into hibernation and even die.

- *Do not count and do not compete.*
  Ideally, relationships are voluntary, rather than a bundle of obligations, contracts, and expectations. Avoid trying to equalize the number of times you have connected with each

other or the number of times you have helped each other. When you count, you judge. When you judge, you make things personal. When you count, you also compete.

- *Listen with an open heart, mind, and spirit.*
  Relationships thrive when people feel heard, understood, and accepted. Do not confuse acceptance with agreement.

- *Do not go overboard.*
  Relationships risk losing authenticity and spontaneity if you act out of proportion to the other. There is no algorithm to determine the correct balance. This is the art of relationships.

- *Appreciate the person and express thanks for the assistance.*
  Relationships are fundamentally about the people, but they also include what people choose to do for each other. Be sure to be grateful for both—the person and the act of kindness or support shown toward you.

- *Give back.*
  Relationships are always a two-way street. As such, you have to get out of yourself at times and focus on what is best for the other person. Intentions are important, but actions—not just the intentions—are felt by others.

HIGHLIGHTS TO RECALL

A large social network does not mean that you feel connected, supported, or appreciated. You may have a few contacts but may still feel connected. Or you may have thousands of connections and feel as if you have to take on life's challenges on your own. Social support works for most people and may help you to cope better with stressful experiences such as a blood draw, a vaccine, or even a needle biopsy.

Try not to expect a single person to meet all your needs for social support. Remember that there are four types of social support.

- Instrumental
- Emotional
- Informational
- Interpersonal

These four types of social support may not be needed for every situation. You have to ask yourself, "Which type of social support do I need to respond to this challenging situation and which person can provide that?"

A key reminder is that social support is a two-way street. On one side of the street, you support others. On the other side of the street, others support you. Please do not count how many times you have supported them or vice versa. Try to support others unconditionally and without the expectation that they will "return the favor." The reality is that most people will return the favor, not out of obligation but out of their heart. What about you?

As you prepare to get vaccinated or go through any other procedure that involves a needle, remember that social support is another tool that can be used to better conquer needle fear or phobia.

TIPS FOR EDUCATORS, HEALTHCARE PROFESSIONALS, AND THERAPISTS

Social support is not a revolutionary new way of influencing the adoption, modification, or elimination of specific health behaviors. Literature clearly demonstrates the influence of adults who accompany children during a blood draw (Taylor, Sellick, & Greenwood, 2011). In my own experience working in a laboratory, I often had to calm the parents down first so that the child would not catch the parents' excessive fear. However, it is also known that if parents provide reassurance to themselves and to their children, the outcomes are far better for all procedures involving needles (McMurtry, 2013).

Intake: Focus on More Than the Chief Complaint and Individual

The intake process that focuses on the social context of the patient or client should incorporate at least three steps beyond the traditional clinical intake process. These three steps are:

- Social History
- Social Network Map or Family Genogram
- Appreciative Inquiry or Discovery

Social History

The first step is to include the social history in the intake process. Wu (2013) recommends that social history should be the first part of the traditional intake rather than the chief complaint or the problem. Wu (2013) argues that putting social history first sets the stage for patient or client education and the promotion of healthy behaviors. It is also important to inquire about the use of social media by the patient or client in order to discover not only social media as a support resource but also the validity and sentiment of the information on the social media sites that they visit.

Social Network Map or Family Genogram

The second step is to map the connections the patient or client has that they deem as supportive in the various ways presented in this chapter. When working with families, a family genogram may be used. Genograms are increasingly being used in healthcare settings (Turabian, 2017).

Appreciative Inquiry or Discovery

The third step is to inquire about the strength of these connections. This could be done by using an appreciative inquiry approach (Cooperrider, Whitney, & Stavros, 2003). Appreciative inquiry falls under the purview of the emerging positive psychology tools. Positive psychology interventions have proven efficacious in several measures, including the overall well-being (Bolier et al., 2013). Furthermore, the benefits of this last beyond the intervention phase (Sin & Lyubomirsky, 2009).

Strengthen Existing Connections and Promote New Connections

Fundamentally, leveraging existing strengths and promoting new connections is the practice of a strength-based approach to therapy or counseling. A strength-based approach is collaborative and goes beyond the relationship between the patient or client and the practitioner, and it also includes "supportive others" who are discovered in the social network map or family genogram. This approach enables the patient or client, the practitioner, and supportive others to be cocreators of the services (Morgan & Ziglio, 2007).

Leveraging Social Media

Social media, like many other areas of life, has some advantages and disadvantages. Social media is broadly defined as a source of social support for many people. A recent meta-analysis suggests that social networking sites (SNS) promote social support and influence in a way that leads to health behavior changes (Laranjo et al., 2014). The mechanism of the action appears to stem from clustering (e.g., connected to others by more than one connection or by redundant ties) and homophily (e.g., hanging out with folks like you). Several existing groups on platforms such as Facebook focus on needle phobia.

REFERENCES

Bolier, L., Haverman, M., Westerhof, G. J., Riper, H., Smit, F., & Bohlmeijer, E. (2013). Positive psychology interventions: A meta-analysis of randomized controlled studies. *BMC Public Health*, 13(1), 119.

Cooperrider, D. L., Whitney, D. K., & Stavros, J. M. (2003). Appreciative inquiry handbook (Vol. 1). Berrett-Koehler.

Laranjo, L., Arguel, A., Neves, A. L., Gallagher, A. M., Kaplan, R., Mortimer, N., ... & Lau, A. Y. (2015). The influence of social networking sites on health behavior change: A systematic review and meta-analysis. *Journal of the American Medical Informatics Association*, 22(1), 243-256.

McMurtry, C. M. (2013). Pediatric needle procedures: Parent–child interactions, child fear, and evidence-based treatment. *Canadian Psychology/Psychologie Canadienne*, 54(1), 75-79.

Morgan, A., & Ziglio, E. (2007). Revitalising the evidence base for public health: An assets model. *International Journal of Health Promotion and Education Supplement*, 2, 17-22.

Sin, N. L., & Lyubomirsky, S. (2009). Enhancing well-being and alleviating depressive symptoms with positive psychology interventions: A practice-friendly meta-analysis. *Journal of Clinical Psychology*, 65(5), 467-487.

Taylor, C., Sellick, K., & Greenwood, K. (2011). The influence of adult behaviors on child coping during venipuncture: A sequential analysis. *Research in Nursing and Health*, 34(2), 116-131.

Turabian, J. L. (2017). Family genogram in general medicine: A soft technology that can be strong. an update. *Research in Medical and Engineering Sciences*, 3(1), 1-6.

Wu, B. J. (2013). History taking in reverse: Beginning with the social history. *Consultant*, 53(1), 34-36.

CONCLUSION

MOVE PAST THIS

I IMAGINE THAT you did not buy this book all that casually. Perhaps the title—*Conquer Needle Phobia: Simple Ways to Reduce Fear and Anxiety*—called you to wake up to your own experience or that of others who may benefit from the evidence-based tips presented in this book.

This book is so close to my heart. When asked to write something on this topic, I found myself reluctant at first, and then I recognized that I could help so many people. Writing this book affirmed my values of social justice and caring for others. How so? Those who have needle phobia or extreme fear of needles may seek the services of a therapist, but this is beyond reach for many because of the cost or a lack of trained therapists. This book is not a replacement for professional help at all, but it does offer evidence-based techniques to educate you about needle fears and phobias as well as possible ways to lessen the negative impact of these fears and phobias on your life.

For, as the book affirms, you are already complete. We all are. Perfectly what we are, including all of our imperfections and inadequacies. The question is: Can we embrace our fear and anxiety to seek and accept help, guidance, and support from others? This is the only question really. And the gut response is: We can, we can...

I hope reading *Conquer Needle Phobia* was a worthwhile experience. I leave you with all that I know about conquering needle fears and phobias. Now your task is to apply this knowledge, reject what doesn't work, and enhance what does.

Be well,
Marty Martin

APPENDIX

LEARN MORE

NO BOOK CAN cover everything. Below is a list of other resources that I recommend you explore. I am a big believer in having a lot of tools in your toolbox and then selecting the tool that works for you. If you find that one tool isn't for you, then go back into your toolbox and get another tool. At times, it's the right tool but the wrong time. Or the right time but the wrong situation.

Books on Needle Fears and Phobias

How to Overcome Fear? Guides to Stop Being Anxious and Worried: Defeat Needle Phobia by Amber Mulkey
Kindle Edition (2021) $8.99 paperback 68 pages

The Needle Phobia Handbook by Karl Rollison
Kindle Edition (2021) $6.99 paperback 142 pages

Watch Out, He Faints: How I Conquered My Phobia of Blood, Needles, and Injections by Brett Kenyon
Kindle Edition (2020) 100 pages

The Diary of a Needle Phobic during Cancer Treatment by Tracey-Portrey Chalmers
$2.99 Kindle 33 pages

Needle Phobia – Fifteen Minute Therapy by James Brackin
CreateSpace Independent Publishing Platform (2013) $14.95 paperback 122 pages

Overcoming Medical Phobias: How to Conquer Fear of Blood, Needles, Doctors, and Dentists by Martin M. Anthony
New Harbinger Publications (2006) $31.71 Paperback 176 pages

Books on Needle Fears and Phobias for Children

Vaccine Comfort: A step-by-step guide for kids, parents, and healthcare providers to improve the vaccine experience by Mary Wilde
2019 $4.99 paperback 32 pages

Shirley and Shaun's Shots by Wendy J. Hall
Wendy J. Hall, 1st edition $9.99 paperback 33 pages

Websites

https://www.needlephobia.com/
This website is chock full of information about needle phobias.

ABOUT THE AUTHOR

MARTY MARTIN, PSYD, is a clinical psychologist, wellness coach, speaker, and writer. He is a professor at DePaul University. He is the author of two books—*The Inner World of Money: Taking Control of Your Financial Decisions and Behavior* and *Taming Disruptive Behavior*. His work has been featured in *USA Today*, *The Washington Post*, and *The Wall Street Journal*.

He has trained groups across the globe, from Groupon in the United Kingdom to Harvard Medical School. He has coached many individuals, from executives to gig workers who desire to stop struggling from fears and anxieties that hold them back from a fulfilling, enjoyable life.

Visit his website at: https://conquerneedlephobia.com/

Printed in Great Britain
by Amazon

80360686R00097